U•X•L Encyclopedia of Weather and Natural Disasters

U·X·L Encyclopedia of Weather and Natural Disasters

Avalanche to El Niño VOLUME 2

Anaxos, Inc., Editors

U·X·L
An imprint of Thomson Gale,
a part of The Thomson Corporation

THOMSON

GALE

Detroit • New York • San Francisco • New Haven, Conn. • Waterville, Maine • London

THOMSON

GALE

U·X·L Encyclopedia of Weather and Natural Disasters

Anaxos, Inc., editors

Project Editor
Melissa Hill

Editorial
Julie Carnagie, Paul Lewon, Lemma Shomali

Indexing Services
Factiva, a Dow Jones & Reuters Company

Rights and Acquisitions
Margaret Abendroth, Margaret Chamberlain-Gaston, Tracie Richardson

Imaging and Multimedia
Lezlie Light, Robyn V. Young

Product Design
Pamela A. Galbreath, Jennifer Wahi

Composition
Evi Seoud, Mary Beth Trimper

Manufacturing
Wendy Blurton, Dorothy Maki

LIBRARY OF CONGRESS CATALOGING-IN-PUBLICATION DATA

UXL encyclopedia of weather and natural disasters / Anaxos, Inc., editors.
    p. cm.
    Includes bibliographical references and index.
    ISBN 978-1-4144-1879-7 (set : alk. paper) -- ISBN 978-1-4144-1880-3 (vol. 1 : alk. paper) --
ISBN 978-1-4144-1881-0 (vol. 2 : alk. paper) -- ISBN 978-1-4144-1882-7 (vol. 3 : alk. paper) --
ISBN 978-1-4144-1883-4 (vol. 4 : alk. paper) -- ISBN 978-1-4144-1884-1 (vol. 5 : alk. paper) --
    1. Meteorology--Encyclopedias, Juvenile. 2. Natural disasters--Encyclopedias, Juvenile.
I. Anaxos, Inc.
    QC854.U95 2008
    551.503--dc22
                                                                                          2007011300

ISBN-13:

978-1-4144-1879-7 (set)	978-1-4144-1882-7 (vol. 3)
978-1-4144-1880-3 (vol. 1)	978-1-4144-1883-4 (vol. 4)
978-1-4144-1881-0 (vol. 2)	978-1-4144-1884-1 (vol. 5)

ISBN-10:

1-4144-1879-5 (set)	1-4144-1882-5 (vol. 3)
1-4144-1880-9 (vol. 1)	1-4144-1883-3 (vol. 4)
1-4144-1881-7 (vol. 2)	1-4144-1884-1 (vol. 5)

This title is also available as an e-book.
ISBN-13 978-1-4144-1885-8, ISBN-10 1-4144-1885-X
Contact your Gale sales representative for ordering information.
Printed in China
10 9 8 7 6 5 4 3 2 1

Table of Contents

Reader's Guide

Weather in all its manifestations—from peaceful blankets of mountain fog to ferocious hurricanes—fascinates most humans. Young children wonder why the sky is blue. Busy professionals wonder whether ice storms will cause flight delays. Backyard gardeners wonder whether their plants will survive a hot, dry summer. *The U•X•L Encyclopedia of Weather and Natural Disasters* presents a comprehensive, up-to-date survey of weather, weather-related topics, and natural disasters that gives readers the science behind the weather events that affect us all every day.

Scope and format

Each of the chapters in this five-volume series presents its topic in clear, nontechnical language. The topics are arranged in alphabetical order. The material is enlivened with eyewitness descriptions of recent weather phenomena, historical accounts of famous past weather events and disasters, biographies of famous figures in meteorology, practical information on handling extreme weather situations, relevant book and film recommendations, and hundreds of photographs, illustrations, and charts. Each chapter also presents step-by-step experiments, suitable for home or classroom, that allow students to have hands-on experiences with the foundations of weather and meteorology. Additionally, *The U•X•L Encyclopedia of Weather and Natural Disasters* provides a "Words to Know" section in each chapter, with key terms clearly defined. A cumulative index and a comprehensive "Where to Learn More" section at the back of each volume give readers easy access to material both within the series and in outside resources.

Volume 1 of this series serves as a general introduction to the topic of weather and natural disasters, and includes chapters on climate, clouds, and precipitation.

Volume 2 presents the first six of the alphabetically arranged chapters on weather and natural disaster topics: Avalanche, Blizzard, Drought, Dust Storm, Earthquake, and El Niño.

Volume 3 presents the following seven chapters: Flood, Fog, Hurricane, Landslide, La Niña, Local Winds, and Monsoon.

Volume 4 wraps up the alphabetically arranged chapters with six more chapters: Optical Effects, Thunderstorm, Tornado, Tsunami, Volcano, and Wildfire.

Volume 5 examines human involvement with weather and natural disasters, offering chapters on forecasting, climate change, and the influence of humans on weather.

Acknowledgements

The development of *The U•X•L Encyclopedia of Weather and Natural Disasters* was a collaborative effort by the staff of Anaxos, Inc., but several key members of the team require special acknowledgement and appreciation. Many thanks are owed to Dr. Elliot Richmond for his broad meteorological expertise and good humor. Special thanks also to Emily Baker-Falconer and Russ Falconer, for their organizational vigor and editorial acumen, and to Liza Banks, for her copyediting prowess.

The staff of Anaxos would also like to thank Gale content project editor Melissa Hill and content product manager Debra Kirby for their guidance, insight, and inspiration.

Also, Melissa Hill would like to thank Lou Camp for additional review of the Climate Change and Global Warming entry. His knowledge of the topic and candid insights contribute much to the final product.

Timeline

c. 1650 B.C.E. The Mediterranean island of Thera is destroyed by a volcanic eruption. The event possibly gives rise to the legend of the lost civilization of Atlantis.

218 B.C.E. Carthaginian leader Hannibal's army is decimated by avalanches as he attempts to cross the Alps with tens of thousands of soldiers and a multitude of war elephants.

350 B.C.E Greek philosopher Aristotle writes *Meteorology.*

79 Eruption of Mount Vesuvius destroys Pompeii and Herculaneum in Italy.

1281 A Chinese fleet of around 4,000 warships is destroyed by a typhoon during an attempted invasion of Japan. The relieved Japanese called the typhoon *kamikaze,* or "divine wind," believing it came from the gods for their protection.

1375 An earthquake destroys the famous lighthouse of Alexandria, Egypt, one of two remaining wonders of the ancient world (the other being the great pyramids of Egypt).

1441 Invention of standardized rain gauge by King Sejong and Prince Munjong of Korea.

1450 Leone Battista Alberti invents first anemometer.

1606 Galileo invents the thermometer.

1643 Evangelista Torricelli invents the barometer.

1657 King Ferdinand II of Tuscany establishes the Accademia Del Cimento of Florence, which develops many early meteorological tools.

1686 English astronomer Edmund Halley publishes a ground-breaking study of trade winds and monsoons.

1707 Mount Fuji in Japan erupts for the last time.

1714 Gabriel Fahrenheit invents the first mercury thermometer.

1742 Swedish astronomer Anders Celsius outlines the centigrade temperature scale. This would lead to what is now the Celsius scale.

1752 Benjamin Franklin performs his famous "kite" experiment, flying a kite that dangled a metal key during a thunderstorm to determine the relationship between lightning and electricity.

1783 Iceland's Mount Laki erupts, spewing massive clouds of ash into the atmosphere and killing up to one fifth of the population of Iceland.

1784 Benjamin Franklin theorizes that the abnormally cold European winter of 1783–1784 was due to the eruption of Mount Laki, becoming one of the first scientists to note the relationship between volcanic eruptions and climate cooling.

1786 Benjamin Franklin publishes an accurate map of the Gulf Stream.

1820 The U.S. Army begins making and recording formal weather observations.

1841 Elias Loomis creates the first synoptic weather map.

1842 James P. Espy is appointed first official U.S. government meteorologist.

1846 Irish astronomer and physicist John Thomas Romney Robinson invents the cup anemometer.

1849 The Smithsonian Institution establishes a national weather observation network using information relayed via telegraph from 150 observers across the country.

1860 As head of the newly established British Meteorological Office, Robert FitzRoy uses the new telegraph system to gather daily observations from across England to make "weather forecasts," a term he coined.

1863 Robert FitzRoy publishes *Weather Book*, an important meteorological text.

1870 President Ulysses S. Grant establishes a national weather warning service under the Secretary of War.

1873 International Meteorological Organization founded.

1875 Benito Vines, the director of the Meteorological Observatory at Belen in Havana, Cuba, issues an accurate hurricane warning two days before a hurricane hits Cuba. His warning saves many lives.

1876 A cyclone in Bangladesh kills more than 200,000.

1883 Eruption of Krakatau causes massive tsunamis that kill 36,000 in Java and Sumatra.

1887 The Yellow River in China floods, killing an estimated one million people.

1889 A dam bursts in Johnstown, Pennsylvania, causing a flood that kills 2,000 people.

1890 U.S. Weather Bureau is founded.

1892 Captain Camilo Carrilo tells the Geographical Society of Lima, Peru, of "El Niño," his term for a warm northerly current and associated climate noticeable around Christmas.

1897 Belgian Adrien de Gerlache sets off for the Antarctic (with a crew that included first-mate Roald Amundsen) to make geographical and meteorological observations of Antarctica. It is the first expedition to spend an entire winter in the Antarctic.

1898 U.S. Weather Bureau establishes a hurricane warning network at Kingston, Jamaica.

1900 A hurricane strikes Galveston, Texas, killing more than 6,000 people.

1902 Stratosphere is discovered. Two scientists, working independently, share credit for the discovery: Richard Assmann and Léon Teisserenc de Bort.

1906 Earthquake in San Francisco kills approximately 3,000.

1919 Introduction of the Norwegian Cyclone Model, a revolutionary method of weather map analysis and interpretation.

1921 Sakuhei Fujiwara publishes a paper on the "Fujiwara Effect," the rotation of two cyclones around each other.

1924 Sir Gilbert Walker coins the term "Southern Oscillation" to describe the current and climate shifts popularly known as El Niño.

1925 The so-called Tri-State Tornado ravages Missouri, Illinois, and Indiana, killing nearly 700 people.

1930 Russian scientist Pavel Mochanov successfully launches his radio-sonde, a balloon-borne device that can take weather measurements and relay them by radio, into the stratosphere.

1934 The "Dust Bowl," a severe drought in southern plains states that lasted several years, begins.

1938 Guy Steward Callendar publishes "The Artificial Production of Carbon Dioxide and Its Influence on Temperature," considered the first description of global warming caused by carbon dioxide emissions.

1943 Pilot J. B. Duckworth intentionally flies into a hurricane off the coast of Texas for the purpose of weather reconnaissance.

1948 First correct tornado prediction made in Oklahoma.

1948 Pacific Tsunami Warning System is established in Honolulu, Hawaii.

1951 The World Meteorological Association, operating as a specialized agency of the United Nations, replaces the International Meteorological Association.

1954 The U.S. National Weather Service begins naming each season's hurricanes alphabetically using female names.

1956 F. K. Ball publishes his theory of the generation of Antarctic katabatic winds.

1959 World's first weather satellite, Vanguard 2, is launched.

1969 The Saffir-Simpson Hurricane Scale is created. The scale rates the strength of hurricanes on a scale of 1 to 5.

1969 Hurricane Camille hits the Gulf Coast of the U.S., killing several hundred people.

1970 The National Oceanic and Atmospheric Administration (NOAA) is established.

1971 Ted Fujita introduces the Fujita scales for rating tornadoes.

1978 Record-breaking blizzard hits northeastern U.S.

1980 Mount St. Helens in Washington State explodes.

1985 Discovery of the Antarctic ozone hole.

2004 Massive tsunami kills nearly 300,000 people in Thailand, India, and Indonesia.

2005 Hurricane Katrina pummels New Orleans and the Mississippi Gulf Coast, killing nearly 2,000 people and forcing millions of people from their homes.

2006 The U.S. experiences a record-breaking wildfire season, with nearly ten million acres burned.

2007 The Enhanced Fujita Scale replaces the Fujita scale as a system for rating tornadoes.

Words to Know

absolute humidity: the amount of water vapor in the air, expressed as a ratio of the amount of water per unit of air.

accretion: the process by which a hailstone grows larger, by gradually accumulating cloud droplets as it travels through a cloud.

acid precipitation: rain and snow that are made more acidic when carbon, sulfur, and/or nitrogen oxides in the air dissolve into water. Also known as acid rain.

acid rain: rain that is made more acidic when carbon, sulfur, and/or nitrogen oxides in the air dissolve into water. Also known as acid precipitation.

active solar collector: system for gathering and storing the Sun's heat that uses pumps and motors. Often used for heating water.

active volcano: a volcano that continues to erupt regularly.

adiabatic process: a process by which the temperature of a moving air parcel changes, even though no heat is exchanged between the air parcel and the surrounding air.

advection: the horizontal movement of a mass such as air or an ocean current.

aftershock: ground shaking that occurs after the main shock of an earthquake.

agricultural report: a specialized weather report tailored to the needs of farmers that includes current temperature, precipitation, and wind speed and direction, as well as frost warnings and predictions of temperature and precipitation for the days to come.

air mass: a large quantity of air throughout which temperature and moisture content is fairly constant.

air pollutant: any harmful substance that exists in the atmosphere at concentrations great enough to endanger the health of living organisms.

air pressure: the pressure exerted by the weight of air over a given area of Earth's surface. Also called atmospheric pressure or barometric pressure.

Air Quality Index (AQI): measurement of air quality, based on concentrations of surface ozone averaged over an eight-hour period for specific locations.

Alps: mountain system composed of more than fifteen principle mountain ranges that extends in an arc for almost 660 miles (1,060 kilometers) across south-central Europe.

anabatic wind: winds caused by warm air close to Earth's surface. The air is less dense than the surrounding air and travels upward along a slope.

Andes: mountain range extending more than 5,000 miles (8,045 kilometers) along the western coast of South America.

anemometer: an instrument that measures wind speed.

aneroid barometer: a type of barometer that consists of a vacuum-sealed metal capsule, within which a spring expands or contracts with changing air pressure.

anvil: the flattened formation at the top of a mature cumulonimbus cloud.

aquifer: an underground layer of spongy rock, gravel, or sand in which water collects.

arid: describes a climate in which almost no rain or snow falls.

ash: very small, fine fragments of lava or rock that are blasted into the air during volcanic explosions.

asthenosphere: region of the mantle below the lithosphere, composed of partially melted rock.

aurora: a bright, colorful display of light in the night sky, produced when charged particles from the Sun enter Earth's atmosphere.

avalanche: a large mass of snow, ice, rocks, soil, or a combination of these elements that moves suddenly and swiftly down a mountain slope, pulled by the force of gravity.

avalanche path: the course an avalanche takes down a slope, composed of a starting zone, a track, and a runout zone.

avalanche wind: a cloudlike mixture of snow particles and air pushed ahead of a slab avalanche as it races downward.

aviation report: a specialized weather report tailored to the needs of pilots that provides information on the height of the clouds, visibility, and storm systems.

backfire: a small fire set by firefighters in the path of an oncoming wildfire to burn up the fuel before the main fire arrives, thus blocking it.

backing wind: a wind that shifts direction, rotating counterclockwise higher in the atmosphere.

barchan dune: a sand dune that, when viewed from above, resembles a crescent moon, with the tips of the crescent pointing downwind. Also called barchane dune, barkhan dune, or crescentic dune.

barograph: an aneroid barometer that records changes in air pressure over time on a rotating drum.

barometer: an instrument used to measure air pressure.

basalt: a type of rock that forms from hardened lava.

blizzard: the most severe type of winter storm, characterized by winds of 35 miles (56 kilometers) per hour or greater, large quantities of falling or blowing snow, and low temperatures.

blocking system: a whirling air mass containing either a high-pressure system (a blocking high) or a low-pressure system (a blocking low), that gets cut off from the main flow of upper-air westerlies.

caldera: a large depression, usually circular or oval shaped, left behind when a volcano's summit collapses.

calvus: "bald"; describes when the upper part of a cloud is losing its rounded, cauliflower-like outline and becoming diffuse and fibrous.

capillatus: "having hair"; a cloud with a cirriform, streaky structure on its upper edges.

castellanus: "castlelike"; used to describe clouds with vertical extensions.

Cenozoic era: the historical period from sixty-five million years ago to the present.

chaos theory: the theory that the weather, by its very nature, is unpredictable. Every time one atmospheric variable (such as heat, air pressure, or water) changes, every other variable also changes—but in ways that are out of proportion with the first variable's change.

chinook: a dry, warm katabatic wind in North America that blows down the eastern side of the Rocky Mountains, from New Mexico to Canada in winter or early spring.

chinook wall cloud: a solid bank of wispy, white clouds that appears over the eastern edge of the Rocky Mountains in advance of a chinook wind.

chlorofluorocarbons (CFCs): compounds similar to hydrocarbons in which one or more of the hydrogen atoms are replaced by fluorine or chlorine.

cinder: a small piece of material thrown from a volcano during an eruption.

cinder cone: a volcanic cone made of lava fragments.

cirriform: a wispy, feathery fair-weather cloud formation that exists at high levels of the troposphere.

cirrostratus: a thin layer of high-altitude clouds that cover most of the sky, but are semitransparent.

cirrus: clouds at high levels of the troposphere, created by wind-blown ice crystals, that are so thin as to be nearly transparent.

Clean Air Act: set of environmental regulations limiting pollutants emitted by cars, factories, and other sources. First enacted by the U.S. Congress in 1970 and updated several times since then.

clear-cutting: the logging practice of harvesting all trees from vast forest tracts.

climate: the weather experienced by a given location, averaged over several decades.

coalescence: the process by which an ice crystal grows larger. The ice crystal collides and sticks together with water droplets as the ice crystal travels down through a cloud.

coastal flood: an overflow of water onto a coastal area caused by a storm surge, strong winds, or tsunami.

cold front: the leading edge of a moving mass of cold air.

cold-phase ENSO (El Niño/Southern Oscillation): another name for La Niña; colder-than-normal eastern Pacific waters.

composite volcano: a volcano with steep sides made of layers of lava and ash.

compressional warming: an adiabatic process by which an air parcel warms as it descends. The descending parcel is compressed by the increasing pressure of the surrounding air, which adds kinetic energy to the molecules. Also called compressional heating.

condensation: the process by which water changes from a gas to a liquid.

condensation nucleus: a tiny solid particle around which condensation of water vapor occurs.

conduction: the transfer of heat by collisions between moving molecules or atoms.

cone: the sloping outer sides of a volcano (not all volcanoes have cones).

conelet: a small cone on the side of a large volcano.

congestus: "congested"; describes clouds with upper parts that are piled up and sharply defined; resembles a head of cauliflower.

conservation tillage: the practice of leaving vegetation on fields during idle periods to protect the soil from erosion and trap moisture.

continental drift: geologic theory that all continents were part of a single, original landmass before they slowly separated and gradually drifted apart.

convection: the upward motion of an air mass or air parcel that has been heated.

convection current: circular movement of a gas or liquid between hot and cold areas.

convective cell: a unit within a thunderstorm cloud that contains updrafts and downdrafts.

convective zone: the region of warm tropical water over which thunderstorms form; the ocean under the Intertropical Convergence Zone.

conventional radar: instrument that detects the location, movement, and intensity of precipitation, and gives indications about the type of precipitation. It operates by emitting microwaves, which are reflected by precipitation. Also called radar.

convergence: the movement of air inward toward a central point, such as the trade winds blowing from the north and south near the equator.

Coriolis effect: the apparent curvature of large-scale winds, ocean currents, and anything else that moves freely across Earth, due to the rotation of Earth around its axis.

corona: a circle of light centered on the Moon or Sun that is usually bounded by a colorful ring or set of rings.

cosmic rays: invisible, high-energy particles that bombard Earth from space.

crater: the bowl-shaped area around the opening at the top of a volcano.

crepuscular rays: bright beams of light that radiate from the Sun and cross the sky.

crest: the highest point of a wave.

critical angle: the angle at which sunlight must strike the back of the raindrop in order to be reflected back to the front of the drop.

crown fire: a fire that spreads through the treetops, or crown, of a forest.

crust: the outermost layer of Earth, varying in thickness from 3.5 miles (5 kilometers) under the ocean to 50 miles (80 kilometers) thick under the continents.

cumuliform: a puffy, heaped-up cloud formation.

cumulonimbus: a tall, vertically developed cloud reaching to the top of the troposphere or above, and capable of producing heavy rain, high winds, and lightning.

cumulus: fluffy, white, mid-level clouds that look like white or light-gray cotton balls of various shapes.

cyclone: a weather system characterized by air that flows inward and circulates around a low-pressure area.

dart leaders: the series of dim lightning strokes that occur immediately after the original lightning stroke, that serve to discharge the remaining buildup of electrons near the base of the cloud.

debris avalanche: a downward slide of loose, earthen material (soil, mud, and small rocks) that begins suddenly and travels at great speeds;

similar to a snow avalanche. It builds into a fearsome mass of mud, trees, and rocks that can cause much damage.

debris slide: a slide of small rocks and shallow layers of loose soil that commonly follows volcanic eruptions.

deforestation: the removal of all or most of the trees from an area.

dendrochronology: the study of the annual growth of rings of trees.

deposition: the process by which water changes directly from a gas to a solid, without first going through the liquid phase.

derecho: a destructive, straight-line wind, which travels faster than 58 mph (93 kph) and has a path of damage at least 280 miles (450 kilometers) long. Also called plow wind.

desert climate: the world's driest climate type, with less than 10 inches (25 centimeters) of rainfall annually.

desert pavement: hard, flat, dry ground and gravel that remain after all sand and dust has been eroded from a surface.

desertification: the process by which semiarid lands turn to desert (also called land degradation). It is caused by prolonged drought, during which time the top layers of soil dry out and blow away.

dew point: the temperature at which a given parcel of air reaches its saturation point and can no longer hold water in the vapor state.

diffraction: the slight bending of sunlight or moonlight around water droplets or other tiny particles.

dispersion: the selective refraction of light that results in the separation of light into the spectrum of colors.

divergence: the movement of air outward, away from a central point.

Doppler radar: a sophisticated type of radar that relies on the Doppler effect, the change in frequency of waves emitted from a moving source, to determine wind speed and direction as well as the direction in which precipitation is moving.

dormant volcano: a volcano that has not erupted for many years.

downburst: an extremely strong, localized downdraft beneath a thunderstorm that spreads horizontally when it hits the ground, destroying objects in its path.

downdraft: a downward blast of air from a thunderstorm cloud, felt at the surface as a cool wind gust.

drizzle: precipitation formed by raindrops between 0.008 inches and 0.02 inches in diameter.

drought: an extended period when the amount of rain or snow that falls on an area is much lower than usual.

dry adiabatic lapse rate: the constant rate at which the temperature of an unsaturated air parcel changes as it ascends or descends through the atmosphere. Specifically, air cools by 5.5°F for every 1,000 feet (1.0°C for every 100 meters) it ascends and warms by 5.5°F for every 1,000 feet (1.0°C for every 100 meters) it descends.

Dust Bowl: the popular name for the approximately 150,000 square-mile-area (400,000-square-kilometer-area) in the southern portion of the Great Plains region of the United States. It is characterized by low annual rainfall, a shallow layer of topsoil, and high winds.

dust devil: a spinning vortex of sand and dust that is usually harmless but may grow quite large. Also called a whirlwind.

dust storm: a large cloud of dust blown by a strong wind.

earthflow: a landslide that consists of material that is moist and full of clay, yet drier than the material in mudflows.

earthquake: a sudden shifting of masses of rock beneath Earth's surface, which releases enormous amounts of energy and sends out shock waves that cause the ground to shake.

eccentricity: the alternating change in shape of Earth's orbit between a circle and an ellipse.

ecosystem: a community of plants and animals, including humans, and their physical surroundings.

effusive eruption: the type of eruption in which lava spills over the side of a crater.

El Niño: Spanish for "the Christ child;" an extraordinarily strong episode (occurring every two to seven years) of the annual warming of the Pacific waters off the coast of Peru and Ecuador.

El Niño/Southern Oscillation (ENSO): the simultaneous warming of the waters of the eastern Pacific and the accompanying shifts in air pressure over the eastern and western Pacific.

electromagnetic spectrum: the array of electromagnetic radiation, which includes radio waves, infrared radiation, visible light, ultra-violet radiation, x rays, and gamma rays.

ENSO: stands for El Niño/Southern Oscillation. It describes the simultaneous warming of the waters in the eastern Pacific Ocean and the shifting pattern of air pressure between the eastern and western edges of the Pacific.

entrainment: the process by which cool, unsaturated air next to a thunderstorm cloud gets pulled into the cloud during the mature stage of a thunderstorm.

Environmental Protection Agency (EPA): government agency charged with implementing the provisions of the Clean Air Act.

epicenter: the point on Earth's surface directly above the focus of an earthquake, where seismic waves first appear.

equinoxes: the days marking the start of spring and fall. Also the two days of the year in which day and night are most similar in length and the Sun appears to cross Earth's equator in its yearly motion.

erosion: the wearing away of a surface by the action of wind, water, or ice.

eruption: the release of pressure that sends lava, rocks, ash, and gases out of a volcano.

evaporation: the process by which water changes from a liquid to a gas.

evaporation fog: fog that is formed when water vapor evaporates into cool air and brings the air to its saturation point.

extinct volcano: a volcano that is never expected to erupt again.

extratropical cyclones: a storm system that forms outside of the tropics and involves contrasting warm and cold air masses.

eye: an area of clear sky and warm, dry, descending air at the center of a hurricane.

eye wall: a vertical area of thick clouds, intense rain, and strong winds marking the outer boundary of the eye.

F

fair-weather waterspout: relatively harmless waterspout that forms over water and arises either in conjunction with, or independently of, a severe thunderstorm. Also called nontornadic waterspout.

fall: the downward motion of rock or soil through the air or along the surface of a steep slope.

Fata Morgana: a special type of superior mirage that takes the form of spectacular castles, buildings, or cliffs rising above cold land or water.

fault: crack in Earth's surface where two plates or sections of the crust push and slide in opposite directions against one another.

fault creep: slow, continuous movement of plates along a fault, allowing pressure to be released.

fibratus: "fibrous"; describes clouds with hairlike strands with no hooks or curls at the end.

fire line: a strip of ground, cleared of all combustible material, that is dug by firefighters to stop the advance of a wildfire. Also called control line.

fire triangle: the combination of three elements required for any fire: fuel, oxygen, and heat.

firestorm: also called a blowup, it is the most explosive and violent type of wildfire.

fissure: a crack in Earth's surface through which volcanic materials can escape.

flash flood: a sudden, intense, localized flooding caused by persistent heavy rainfall or the failure of a levee or dam.

floccus: "flock of wool"; describes clouds with small tufts with ragged undersides.

flood: an overflow of water on land that is normally dry.

flood basalt: high temperature basaltic lava that flows from a fissure in Earth's crust and covers large areas of the landscape. Also known as plateau basalt.

focus: the underground starting place of an earthquake, also called the hypocenter.

fog: a cloud that forms near or on the ground.

food chain: the transfer of food energy from one organism to another. It begins with a plant species, which is eaten by an animal species; it continues with a second animal species, which eats the first, and so on.

foreshock: ground shaking that occurs before the main shock of an earthquake.

fossil fuels: coal, oil, and natural gas—materials composed of the remains of plants or animals that covered Earth millions of years ago and are today burned for fuel.

fractus: "fractured"; describes clouds with broken up, ragged edges.

freezing nuclei: a tiny particle of ice or other solid onto which super-cooled water droplets can freeze.

front: the dividing line between two air masses of different temperatures.

frontal system: a weather pattern that accompanies an advancing front.

frostbite: the freezing of the skin.

fuel cell: device that generates electricity by combining hydrogen and oxygen; it emits water vapor as a by-product.

Fujita Intensity scale: scale that measures tornado intensity, based on wind speed and the damage created.

fumarole: a vent in Earth's surface that releases steam and other gases, but generally no lava.

funnel cloud: cone-shaped spinning column of air that hangs well below the base of a thunderstorm cloud.

gale-force wind: any wind whose sustained speed is between 39 and 54 mph (63 and 87 kph).

geologist: a scientist who studies the origin, history, and structure of Earth.

geostationary satellite: weather satellite that remains above a given point on Earth's equator, traveling at the same speed as Earth's rotation about 22,300 miles (35,900 kilometers) above the surface.

geyser: a regular spray of hot water and steam from underground into the air.

glacier: slowly flowing masses of ice created by years of snowfall and cold temperatures.

global warming: the theory that average temperatures around the world have begun to rise, and will continue to rise, due to an increase of certain gases, called greenhouse gases, in the atmosphere. Also called enhanced greenhouse effect and global climate change.

global water budget: the balance of the volume of water coming and going between the oceans, atmosphere, and continental landmasses.

glory: a set of colored rings that appears on the top surface of a cloud, directly beneath the observer. A glory is formed by the interaction of sunlight with tiny cloud droplets and is most often viewed from an airplane.

Great Depression: the worst economic collapse in the history of the modern world. It began with the stock market crash of 1929 and lasted through the late 1930s.

green flash: a very brief flash of green light that appears near the top edge of a rising or setting Sun.

greenhouse effect: the warming of Earth due to the presence of greenhouse gases, which trap upwardly radiating heat and return it to Earth's surface.

greenhouse gases: gases that trap heat in the atmosphere. The most abundant greenhouse gases are water vapor and carbon dioxide. Others include methane, nitrous oxide, and chlorofluorocarbons.

ground blizzard: the drifting and blowing of snow that occurs after a snowfall has ended.

ground fire: a fire that burns beneath the layer of dead plant material on the forest floor.

gust front: the dividing line between cold downdrafts and warm air at the surface, characterized by strong, cold, shifting winds.

haboob: a tumbling black wall of sand that has been stirred up by cold downdrafts along the leading edge of a thunderstorm or cold front. It occurs in north-central Africa and the southwestern United States.

hail: precipitation comprised of hailstones.

hailstone: frozen precipitation that is either round or has a jagged surface, is either totally or partially transparent and ranges in size from that of a pea to that of a softball.

hair hygrometer: an instrument that measures relative humidity. It uses hairs (human or horse) that grow longer and shorter in response to changing humidity.

halo: a thin ring of light that appears around the Sun or Moon, caused by the refraction of light by ice crystals.

harmattan: a mild, dry, and dusty wind that originates in the Sahara Desert.

haze: the uniform, milky-white appearance of the sky that results when humidity is high and there are a large number of particles in the air.

heat cramps: muscle cramps or spasms, usually afflicting the abdomen or legs, that may occur during exercise in hot weather.

heat exhaustion: a form of mild shock that results when fluid and salt are lost through heavy perspiration.

heat stroke: a life-threatening condition that sets in when heat exhaustion is left untreated and the body has spent all its efforts to cool itself. Also called sunstroke.

heat wave: an extended period of high heat and humidity.

heating-degree-days: the number of degrees difference between the day's mean (average) temperature and the temperature at which most people set their thermostats. The total number of heating-degree-days in a season is an indicator of how much heating fuel has been consumed.

heavy snow: snowfall that reduces visibility to 0.31 mile (0.5 kilometer) and yields, on average, 4 inches (10 centimeters) or more in a twelve-hour period or 6 inches (15 centimeters) or more in a twenty-four-hour period.

hollow column: a snowflake in the shape of a long, six-sided column.

Holocene: the most recent part of the Cenozoic era, from ten thousand years ago to the present.

horse latitudes: a high-pressure belt that exists at around 30° latitude, north and south, where air from the equatorial region descends and brings clear skies.

hot spot: an area beneath Earth's crust where magma currents rise.

hotshot: a specialized firefighter who ventures into hazardous areas and spends long hours battling blazes.

humilis: "humble" or "lowly"; describes clouds with a small, flattened appearance.

humiture index: an index that combines temperature and relative humidity to determine how hot it actually feels and, consequently, how stressful outdoor activity will be. Also called temperature-humidity index or heat index.

hurricane: the most intense form of tropical cyclone. A hurricane is a storm that forms in the northern Atlantic Ocean or in the eastern Pacific Ocean. It is made up of a series of tightly coiled bands of thunderstorm clouds, with a well-defined pattern of rotating winds and maximum sustained winds greater than 74 mph (119 kph).

hurricane warning: hurricane landfall is imminent.

hurricane watch: hurricane landfall is possible.

hurricane-force wind: sustained winds greater than 74 mph (119 kph).

hygrometer: an instrument used to measure relative humidity. It consists of a dry-bulb thermometer and a wet-bulb thermometer. Also called psychrometer.

hypothermia: a condition characterized by a drop in core body temperature from the normal 98.6°F (37°C) to 95°F (35°C) or lower.

ice age: a period during which significant portions of Earth's surface are covered with ice.

igneous rock: rock made of solidified molten material that made its way from the interior of the planet to the surface.

incus: "anvil" or "fan-shaped"; describes a cloud with a spreading, smooth or fibrous mass at the top.

induction: the process whereby excess electrical charges in one object cause the accumulation by displacement of electrical charges with the opposite charge in another nearby object.

inferior mirage: a mirage that appears as an inverted, lowered image of a distant object. It typically forms in hot weather.

insulator: a substance through which electricity does not readily flow.

intensity: description of the physical damage caused by an earthquake.

interglacial period: a relatively warm period that exists between two ice ages.

Intertropical Convergence Zone: a belt of warm, rising, unstable air formed from the inward-flowing trade winds from north and south of the equator.

intortis: "intertwined"; describes clouds with entangled, fibrous strands.

inversion, atmospheric: a stable reversal of the normal pattern of atmospheric temperature, formed when a warm air mass sits over a cold air mass near the surface.

ion: an atom that has lost or gained an electron, thereby acquiring a positive or negative electrical charge.

iridescence: an irregular patch of colored light on a cloud.

isobar: an imaginary line that connects areas of equal air pressure, after the air pressure measurements have been adjusted to sea level.

isotherm: an imaginary line connecting areas of similar temperature.

jet stream: the world's fastest upper-air winds. Jet streams travel in a west-to-east direction, at speeds of 80 to 190 miles (130 to 300 kilometers) per hour, around 30,000 feet (9,150 meters) above the ground. Jet streams occur where the largest differences in air temperature and air pressure exist. In North America, jet streams are typically found over southern Canada and the northern United States, as well as over the southern United States and Mexico. The northern jet stream is called the polar jet stream, and the southern jet stream is called the subtropical jet stream.

katabatic wind: a strong wind that travels down a mountain under the force of gravity, and is stronger than a valley breeze.

khamsin: a hot, dry, southerly wind that originates on the Sahara and produces large sand and dust storms.

kinetic energy: the energy of motion.

La Niña: Spanish for little girl, a period of cooler-than-normal water temperatures in the eastern Pacific near the coast of Peru and Ecuador. It often follows an El Niño.

lahar: a mudflow of volcanic ash and water that sometimes occurs after a volcanic eruption.

lake breeze: a wind similar to a sea breeze that can be felt at the edge of a large lake.

landfall: the point on a coast where the center of a hurricane first crosses.

landslide: the movement of large amounts of soil, rocks, mud, and other debris downward and outward along a slope.

latent heat: the heat that must be removed from a quantity of water vapor to cause it to turn into a liquid, or that must be added to a quantity of liquid water to cause it to turn into a vapor; called latent because the temperature of the quantity of water or water vapor does not change.

latitude: an imaginary line encircling Earth, parallel to the equator, that tells one's position north or south on the globe.

lava: molten rock that erupts from a fissure or a vent (*see* magma).

lava domes: volcanic formations built up from layers of viscous lava that does not flow far from its source.

lava tube: a tube formed when an outer layer of lava is cooled by the air and hardens and molten lava then flows out of the middle of the tube, leaving it hollow.

leeward: the opposite direction from which the wind is blowing. Also the slope of a mountain opposite to the direction of local or prevailing winds down which cold air descends, producing dry conditions.

lenticularis: "lens-shaped"; describes clouds that are elongated, or almond-shaped with well-defined outlines.

lightning: a short-lived, bright flash of light during a thunderstorm that is produced by a 100-million-volt electrical discharge in the atmosphere.

liquefaction: the transformation of water-saturated soil into a liquidlike mass, usually by the action of seismic waves.

lithosphere: the rigid outermost region of Earth, composed of the crust and the upper part of the mantle.

local winds: winds that blow across surface areas ranging from a few miles to about 100 miles (about 160 kilometers) in width. Also known as mesoscale winds or regional winds.

loose-snow avalanche: avalanche composed of loosely packed snow that begins at a single point and slides down a slope, fanning out in the shape of an inverted V.

magma: molten rock containing dissolved gas and crystals that originates deep within Earth. When it reaches the surface it is called lava.

magma chamber: a reservoir of magma beneath Earth's surface.

magnitude: the power of an earthquake, as recorded by a seismograph, or seismometer.

mammatus: round, pouchlike cloud formations that appear in clusters and hang from the underside of a larger cloud.

mantle: the thick, dense layer of rock that lies beneath Earth's crust. The mantle is about 1,800 miles (2,900 kilometers) thick and accounts for about 84 percent of Earth's volume.

marine forecast: a specialized weather forecast of interest to coastal residents and mariners, which gives projections of the times of high and low tide, wave height, wind speed and direction, and visibility.

Maunder minimum: a period of time from 1645 to 1715, during which sunspot activity was almost nonexistent.

mediocris: "mediocre"; describes clouds of moderate vertical development with lumpy tops.

mesocyclone: region of rotating updrafts created by wind shear within a supercell storm; it may be the beginnings of a tornado.

mesoscale winds: winds that blow across surface areas ranging from a few miles to about 100 miles (about 160 kilometers) in width. Also known as local winds or regional winds.

Mesozoic era: the historical period from 225 million years ago to 65 million years ago, best known as the age of the dinosaurs.

meteorologist: a scientist who studies weather and climate.

meteorology: the scientific study of the atmosphere and atmospheric processes, namely weather and climate.

middle latitudes: the regions of the world that lie between the latitudes of 30° and 60° north and south. Also called temperate regions.

Milankovitch theory: the theory stating that the three types of variation in Earth's orbit, taken together, can be linked with warm and cold periods throughout history. These variations include: the shape of Earth's orbit, the direction of tilt of its axis, and the degree of tilt of its axis.

mirage: an optical illusion in which an object appears in a position that differs from its true position, or a nonexistent object (such as a body of water) appears.

modified Mercalli scale: scale developed by Italian seismologist Giuseppe Mercalli to measure the intensity of an earthquake based on the amount of vibration felt by people and the extent of damage to buildings.

moist adiabatic lapse rate: the variable rate at which the temperature of a saturated air parcel changes as it ascends or descends through the atmosphere.

monsoon: a name for seasonal winds that result in a rainy season occurring in the summer on tropical continents, when the land becomes warmer than the sea beside it.

monsoon climate: a climate that is warm year-round with very rainy (flood-prone) summers and relatively dry winters. It encompasses much of southern and southeastern Asia, the Philippines, coastal regions of northern South America, and slices of central Africa.

mountain breeze: a gentle downhill wind that forms at night as cold, dense, surface air travels down a mountainside and sinks into the valley. Also called gravity wind or drainage wind.

mud slide: a landslide of mostly mud mixed with debris, often caused by heavy rains on steep land with sparse vegetation.

mudflow: a landslide consisting of soil mixed with water. It is wetter than the material in an earthflow.

multi-cell thunderstorm: a thunderstorm system that contains several convective cells.

multi-vortex tornado: tornado in which the vortex divides into several smaller vortices called suction vortices.

nebulosus: "nebulous"; describes clouds that are a thin, hazy veil.

NEXRAD: acronym for Next Generation Weather Radar, the network of high-powered Doppler radar units that cover the continental United States, Alaska, Hawaii, Guam, and South Korea.

nor'easter: a strong, northeasterly wind that brings cold air, often accompanied by heavy rain, snow, or sleet, to the coastal areas of New England and the mid-Atlantic states. Also called northeaster.

Northern Hemisphere: the half of the Earth that lies north of the equator.

numerical prediction model: a computer program that mathematically duplicates conditions in nature. It is often used to predict the weather.

obliquity: the angle of the tilt of Earth's axis in relation to the plane of its orbit.

occluded front: a front formed by the interaction of three air masses: one cold, one cool, and one warm. The result is a multi-tiered air system, with cold air wedged on the bottom, cool air resting partially on top of the cold air, and warm air on the very top.

ocean currents: the major routes through which ocean water is circulated around the globe.

oceanography: the study and exploration of the ocean.

Organized Convection Theory: a widely accepted model of hurricane formation.

orographic lifting: the upward motion of warm air that occurs when a warm air mass travels up the side of a mountain.

orographic thunderstorm: a type of air mass thunderstorm that's initiated by the flow of warm air up a mountainside. Also called mountain thunderstorm.

orographic uplift: the forcing of air upward, caused by the movement of air masses over mountains.

oxidation: a chemical reaction involving the combination of a material with oxygen.

ozone days: days on which the smog threshold is surpassed.

ozone hole: the region above Antarctica where the ozone concentration in the upper atmosphere gets very low at the end of each winter.

ozone layer: the layer of Earth's atmosphere, between 25 and 40 miles (40 and 65 kilometers) above ground, that filters out the Sun's harmful rays. It contains a higher concentration of ozone, which is a form of oxygen that has three atoms per molecule.

paleoclimatologist: a scientist who studies climates of the past.

Paleozoic era: the historical period from 570 million years ago to 225 million years ago.

particulates: small particles suspended in the air and responsible for most atmospheric haze. Particulates can irritate the lungs and cause lung disease with long exposure.

passive solar collector: system for collecting and storing the Sun's heat that has no moving parts and is generally used for home heating.

period: the time between two successive waves.

permafrost: a layer of subterranean soil that remains frozen year-round.

photochemical smog: a hazy layer containing ozone and other gases that sometimes appears brown. It is produced when pollutants that are released by car exhaust fumes react with strong sunlight.

photovoltaic cell: light-sensitive device containing semiconductor crystals (materials that conduct an electric current under certain conditions) that convert sunlight to electricity. Also called solar cells.

phytoplankton: tiny marine plants that occupy the lowest level of the food chain.

pileus: "felt cap"; small cap- or hood-shaped formation perched above or attached to the top of a cloud.

pipe: a narrow passageway that leads from a magma reservoir to a vent.

plate: a large section of Earth's crust.

plate tectonics: the geologic theory that Earth's crust is composed of rigid plates that are in constant motion with respect to each other, creating the major geologic features on the planet's surface.

Plinian eruption: a volcanic eruption that releases a deadly cloud of gas, dust, and ash.

polar easterlies: cold, global winds that travel across the polar regions, from the northeast to the southwest in the Northern Hemisphere and from the southeast to the northwest in the Southern Hemisphere.

polar front: the region or boundary separating air masses of polar origin from those of tropical or subtropical origin.

polar jet stream: a North American jet stream, typically found over southern Canada or the northern United States.

polar orbiting satellite: a weather satellite that travels in a north-south path, crossing over both poles just 500 to 625 miles (800 to 1,000 kilometers) above Earth's surface.

precession of the equinoxes: the reversal of the seasons every thirteen thousand years. This occurs because Earth spins about its axis like a top in slow motion and wobbles its way through one complete revolution every twenty-six thousand years.

precipitation: water particles that originate in the atmosphere (usually referring to water particles that form in clouds) and fall to the ground as rain, snow, ice pellets, or hail.

prescribed burn: a planned, controlled fire that clears flammable debris from the forest floor.

pressure gradient: the difference in air pressure between a high and low pressure area relative to the distance separating them.

psychrometer: an instrument used to measure relative humidity. It consists of a dry-bulb thermometer and a wet-bulb thermometer. Also called hygrometer.

Pulaski: a combination ax and hoe that is used by firefighters to clear brush and create a fire line. It was invented by forest ranger Edward Pulaski in 1903.

pumice: volcanic rock formed during the explosive eruption of magma; it has numerous gas bubbles and may float on water.

pyroclastic flow: a rapid flow of hot material consisting of ash, pumice, other rock fragments, and gas ejected by an explosive eruption.

radar: an instrument that detects the location, movement, and intensity of precipitation, and gives indications about the type of precipitation. It operates by emitting microwaves, which are reflected by precipitation. It is an abbreviation for **Ra**dio **D**etection **a**nd **R**anging. Radar may be called conventional radar to distinguish it from Doppler radar.

radiational cooling: the loss of heat from the ground upward into the atmosphere.

radioactive dating: a technique used to determine the age of rocks that contain radioactive elements, which works on the principle that radioactive nuclei emit high-energy particles over time.

radiosonde: an instrument package carried aloft on a small helium- or hydrogen-filled balloon. It measures temperature, air pressure, and relative humidity from the ground to a maximum height of 19 miles (30 kilometers).

rain band: a band of heavy thunderstorms forming a tightly coiled spiral around the center of a tropical storm.

rain gauge: a container that catches rain and measures the amount of rainfall.

rain shadow effect: the uneven distribution of precipitation across a mountain, with most of the precipitation falling on the windward side and very little falling on the leeward side.

rainbow: an arc of light, separated into its constituent colors, that stretches across the sky.

research buoy: a tethered or drifting buoy placed in the open ocean capable of recording atmospheric and ocean conditions and transmitting them to a satellite.

reflection: the process by which light both strikes a surface, and bounces off that surface, at the same angle.

refraction: the bending of light as it is transmitted between two transparent media of different densities.

regeneration: the process of making or starting anew.

relative humidity: a measure of humidity as a percentage of the total moisture a given volume of air, at a particular temperature, can hold.

Richter scale: the scale developed by American seismologist Charles Richter that describes the amount of energy released by an earthquake on a scale from 1 to 10. Each whole number increase in value on the scale indicates a ten-fold increase in the energy released. Earthquakes measuring 7 to 7.9 are major and those measuring 8 or above cause widespread destruction.

ridge: a northward crest in the wavelike flow of upper-air westerlies, within which exists a high pressure area.

Ring of Fire: the name given to the geologically active belt that surrounds the Pacific Ocean and is home to more than 75 percent of the world's volcanoes.

river flood: a flood caused when a river spills over its banks.

rock slide: a cascade of rocks (of any size) down a steep slope at high speeds.

roll cloud: a cloud that looks like a giant, elongated cylinder lying on its side, that is rolling forward. It follows in the wake of a gust front.

Saffir-Simpson Hurricane Damage Potential scale: a scale devised by Herbert Saffir and Robert Simpson intended to be used to predict a hurricane's destructive potential.

saltation: the wind-driven movement of particles along the ground and through the air.

saturated: air that contains all of the water vapor it can hold at a given temperature; 100 percent relative humidity.

saturation point: the point at which a given volume of air contains the maximum possible amount of water vapor.

scattering: multidirectional reflection of light by minute particles in the air.

sea breeze: the gentle wind that blows from over the sea to the shore during the day, due to differences in air pressure above each surface.

season: a period of the year characterized by certain weather conditions, such as temperature and precipitation, as well as the number of hours of sunlight each day.

sector plate: a star-shaped snowflake.

seismic waves: vibrations that move outward from the focus of an earthquake, causing the ground to shake.

seismograph: instrument used to detect and measure seismic waves. Also known as a seismometer.

semiarid: a climate in which very little rain or snow falls.

semipermanent highs and lows: the four large pressure areas (two high-pressure and two low-pressure), situated throughout the Northern Hemisphere, that undergo slight shifts in position, and major changes in strength, throughout the year.

severe blizzard: a blizzard in which wind speeds exceed 45 miles (72 kilometers) per hour, snowfall is heavy, and the temperature is 10°F (−12°C) or lower.

severe thunderstorm: a thunderstorm with wind gusts of at least 58 mph (93 kph); hailstones at least 3/4 inch (2 centimeters) in diameter; or tornadoes or funnel clouds.

shamal: a hot, dry, dusty wind that blows for one to five days at a time, producing great dust storms throughout the Persian Gulf.

shelf cloud: a fan-shaped cloud with a flat base that forms along the edge of a gust front.

shield volcano: a volcano with long, gentle slopes, built primarily by lava flows.

shower: a brief spell of localized rainfall, possibly heavy, that only occurs in warm weather.

simoom: a hot, dry, blustery, dust-laden wind that blows across the Sahara and the deserts of Israel, Syria, and the Arabian peninsula.

sinkhole: a natural, steep depression in a land surface caused by collapse of a cavern roof.

skin cancer: a disease of the skin caused primarily by exposure to the ultraviolet rays in sunlight.

slab avalanche: avalanche that begins when fracture lines develop in a snowpack and a large surface plate breaks away, then crumbles into blocks as it falls down a slope.

sling psychrometer: an instrument that measures relative humidity. It consists of a dry-bulb thermometer and a wet-bulb thermometer mounted side by side on a metal strip, which rotates on a handle at one end.

slump: the slow downhill movement of large portions (called blocks) of a slope. Each block rotates backward toward the slope in a series of curving movements.

smog: common name for photochemical smog—a layer of hazy, brown air pollution at Earth's surface comprised of ozone and other chemicals.

smog threshold: the level of smog allowed by law and set by the Environmental Protection Agency at 80 parts per billion (ppb) of surface ozone.

smokejumper: a specialized firefighter who parachutes to strategic locations from airplanes to battle wildfires.

snow fence: a device placed in fields and along highways that slows the wind and reduces the blowing and drifting of snow.

solifluction: the most rapid type of earthflow, occurring when snow or ice thaws or when earthquakes produce shocks that turn the soil into a fluid-like mass.

Southern Oscillation: shifting patterns of air pressure at sea level, between the eastern and western edges of the Pacific Ocean.

spissatus: "tightly packed"; describes icy formations at the top of a vertical cloud that are dense enough to block out the Sun.

spotting: the starting of new fires, called spot fires, by sparks and embers that drift ahead of an advancing wildfire.

squall line: a moving band of strong thunderstorms.

stable air layer: an atmospheric layer through which an air parcel cannot rise or descend.

stationary front: a boundary between two air masses at different temperatures which are not moving or are moving slowly.

steam eruption: a violent eruption that occurs when water comes in contact with magma, rapidly turns to steam, and causes the mixture to explode.

stepped leader: an invisible stream of electrons that initiates a lightning stroke. A stepped leader surges from the negatively charged region of a cloud, down through the base of the cloud, and travels in a stepwise fashion toward the ground.

storm surge: an abnormal rise of the sea over and above normal tides and due to strong winds and low pressure accompanying a storm or hurricane.

stratiformis: "covering" or "blanket"; describes clouds that form a thick layer.

stratosphere: the second-lowest layer of Earth's atmosphere, from about 9 to 40 miles (15 to 65 kilometers) above ground.

stratus: gloomy, gray, featureless sheets of clouds that cover the entire sky, at low levels of the atmosphere.

subduction zone: a region where two plates come together and the edge of one plate slides beneath the other.

subsidence: a gradual sinking of the land surface relative to its previous level.

subtropical jet stream: a North American jet stream, typically found over the southern United States or northern Mexico.

suction vortices: small vortices within a single tornado that continually form and dissipate as the tornado moves along, creating the tornado's strongest surface winds.

sunspot: an area of magnetic disturbance on the surface of the Sun, sometimes referred to as a sun storm.

supercell storm: the most destructive and long-lasting form of a severe thunderstorm, arising from a single, powerful convective cell. It is characterized by strong tornadoes, heavy rain, and hail the size of golf balls or larger.

supercooled water: water that remains in the liquid state below the freezing point.

superior mirage: a cold-weather mirage that appears as a taller and closer, and sometimes inverted, image of a distant object.

surface fire: a fire with a visible flame that consumes plant material and debris on the forest floor.

thermal: a pocket of rising, warm air that is produced by uneven heating of the ground.

thermograph: an instrument consisting of a thermometer and a needle that etches on a rotating drum, continually recording the temperature.

thermometer: an instrument used to measure temperature. It consists of a vacuum-sealed narrow glass tube with a bulb in the bottom containing mercury or red-dyed alcohol. Also called dry-bulb thermometer.

thunderstorm: a relatively small but intense storm system resulting from strong rising air currents; characterized by heavy rain or hail along with thunder, lightning, and sometimes tornadoes.

tidal station: a floating instrument center in the ocean that records water levels.

topography: the shape and height of Earth's surface features.

tornadic waterspout: tornado that forms over land and travels over water. Tornadic waterspouts are relatively rare and are the most intense form of waterspouts.

tornado: rapidly spinning column of air that extends from a thunderstorm cloud to the ground. Also called a twister.

tornado cyclone: spinning column of air that protrudes through the base of a thunderstorm cloud.

tornado family: a group of tornadoes that develop from a single thunderstorm.

tornado outbreak: emergence of a tornado family. Tornado outbreaks are responsible for the greatest amount of tornado-related damage.

trade winds: dominant surface winds near the equator, generally blowing from east to west and toward the equator.

translucidus: "translucent"; describes clouds that form a transparent layer covering a large part of the sky, through which the Sun or Moon shines.

transpiration: the process by which plants emit water through tiny pores in the underside of their leaves.

transverse dune: a series of connected barchan dunes, which appear as tall, elongated crescents of sand running perpendicular to the prevailing wind.

tropical cyclone: any rotating weather system that forms over tropical waters.

tropical depression: a storm with rotating bands of clouds and thunderstorms and maximum sustained winds of less than 38 miles (61 kilometers) per hour.

tropical disturbance: a cluster of thunderstorms that is beginning to demonstrate a cyclonic circulation pattern.

tropical storm: a tropical cyclone weaker than a hurricane, with organized bands of rotating thunderstorms and maximum sustained winds of 39 to 73 mph (63 to 117 kph).

tropical wave: an elongated area of low air pressure, oriented north to south, causing areas of cloudiness and thunderstorms.

tropics: the region of Earth between 23.5° north latitude and 23.5° south latitude.

tropopause: the boundary between the troposphere and the stratosphere, between 30,000 and 40,000 feet (9,000 and 12,000 meters) above ground.

troposphere: the lowest atmospheric layer, where clouds exist and virtually all weather occurs.

trough: a southward dip in the wavelike flow of upper-air westerlies, within which exists a low-pressure area. Also, the lowest point of a wave.

tsunami: a huge ocean wave that can travel at speeds up to 600 mph (965 kph) for hundreds of miles over open ocean before it hits land; caused by an earthquake, underwater volcanic eruption, or underwater landslide.

tsunami warning: an alert stating that a tsunami has been detected and is approaching the designated area. People are instructed to move to higher ground immediately.

tsunami watch: an alert stating that an earthquake has occurred with sufficient magnitude to trigger a tsunami. People are instructed to listen for further news.

typhoon: tropical cyclone that form in the China Sea or in the western North Pacific Ocean.

uncinus: "hook-shaped"; describes clouds with fibers creating the pattern called "mare's tail."

undulatus: "undulating"; describes clouds with wavelike formation within patches, layers, or sheets.

unhealthy air days: days on which surface ozone levels reach 80 parts per billion—a concentration considered unhealthy to children, people with respiratory problems, and adults who exercise or work vigorously outdoors.

unsaturated air: air that has less than 100 percent relative humidity.

updraft: a column of air blowing upward inside a vertical cloud.

upper-air westerlies: global-scale, upper-air winds that flow in waves heading west to east (but also shifting north and south) through the middle latitudes of the Northern Hemisphere.

upwelling: the rising up of cold waters from the depths of the ocean, replacing the warm surface water that has moved away horizontally.

valley breeze: an uphill wind that forms during the day as the valley air is heated and rises. Also called anabatic wind.

veering wind: a wind that shifts direction, turning clockwise as it moves higher.

vent: an opening in the surface of Earth through which molten rock, lava, ash, and gases escape.

ventifact: a rock, boulder, or canyon wall that has been sculpted by wind and wind-blown sand.

vertical cloud: a cloud that develops upward to great heights. Vertical clouds are the products of sudden, forceful uplifts of small pockets of warm air.

virga: rain that falls from clouds but evaporates in midair under conditions of very low humidity.

volcano: an opening in the surface of Earth (vent) through which molten rock, lava, ashes, and gases escape; it is also the name for the mountain or hill that is formed by the lava and other erupted material.

vortex: (plural: vortices) vertical axis of extremely low pressure around which winds rotate.

wall cloud: a roughly circular, rotating cloud that protrudes from the base of a thunderstorm cloud; it is often the beginning of a tornado.

warm front: the line behind which a warm air mass is advancing, and in front of which a cold air mass is retreating.

warm-phase ENSO (El Niño/Southern Oscillation): another name for El Niño; warmer-than-normal eastern Pacific waters.

warning: a severe weather advisory that means that a storm has been sighted and may strike a specific area.

watch: a severe weather advisory that means that while a storm does not yet exist, conditions are ripe for one to develop.

waterspout: rapidly rotating column of air that forms over a large body of water, extending from the base of a cloud to the surface of the water.

weather: the set of conditions of temperature, humidity, cloud cover, and wind speed at a given time.

weather aircraft: aircraft that carry weather instruments and collect data in the upper levels of the troposphere. They are primarily used to probe storm clouds, within which they measure temperature, air pressure, and wind speed and direction.

weather forecast: a prediction of what the weather will be like in the future, based on present and past conditions.

weather map: a map of a large geographic region, on which weather station entries are plotted. By looking at a weather map, a meteorologist can determine the locations of fronts, regions of high and low pressure, the dividing line between temperatures below freezing and above freezing, and the movement of storm systems. Also called surface analysis.

weather satellite: a satellite equipped with infrared and visible imaging equipment that provides views of storms and continuously monitors weather conditions around the planet.

westerlies: global-scale surface winds that travel from the southwest to the northeast in the Northern Hemisphere, and from the northwest to the southeast in the Southern Hemisphere, between about 30° and 60° latitude.

whiteout: a condition in which falling, drifting, and blowing snow reduces visibility to almost zero.

wildfire: a large, uncontrolled fire in grass, brush, or trees.

wind farm: a large group of interconnected wind turbines.

wind power: power, in the form of electricity, derived from the wind.

wind shear: a condition in which a vertical layer of air is sandwiched between two other vertical layers, each of which is traveling at a different speed and/or direction, causing the sandwiched air layer to roll.

wind sock: a cone-shaped cloth bag open on both ends, through which wind flows that is used to determine the direction and estimate the speed of the wind.

wind speed: the rate at which air is moving relative to the ground.

wind turbine: a windmill designed to convert the kinetic energy of wind into electrical energy.

wind wave: a wave caused by the action of wind on the water surface.

windbreak: row of trees or shrubs placed in a farm field to slow the wind and keep it from blowing away the soil.

windchill equivalent temperature: the temperature at which the body would lose an equivalent amount of heat, if there were no wind. Also called windchill index.

windchill factor: the cooling effect on the body due to a combination of wind and temperature.

windward: the direction from which the wind is blowing. Also the slope of a mountain on the side of local or prevailing winds, up which the air cools as it ascends producing moist, cloudy, or rainy conditions.

Avalanche

An avalanche is a large mass of snow, ice, rocks, soil, or a combination of these elements that moves suddenly and swiftly down a mountain slope, pulled by the force of gravity. It destroys nearly everything in its path. The most common type of avalanche is a snow avalanche. An estimated 100,000 snow avalanches occur in the United States each year. Ice and debris avalanches, while they occur less frequently, are far more dangerous and cause greater damage than snow avalanches.

The Mount Huascarán avalanche of 1962

In the early evening of January 10, 1962, a huge mass of ice measuring about 2.5 million cubic yards (1.9 million cubic meters; the size of a football stadium filled from bottom to top) and weighing approximately 3 million tons (2.7 million metric tons; the weight of six thousand steam locomotives) broke loose from the glacier-capped peak of Mount Huascarán (pronounced wass-ka-RON), the tallest mountain in Peru. As the ice mass hurtled down the cliff face toward the populated valley below, it gained speed and grew in size, picking up rocks and other debris. After traveling nearly 10 miles (16 kilometers) in eight minutes, the mass came to a halt. In its wake, it left a carpet of ice, mud, and rock that covered ten villages and towns, ten thousand livestock, and almost four thousand people.

Mount Huascarán (*Nevado Huascarán* in Spanish) is part of the Andes, a 5,000-mile-long (8,045-kilometers-long) mountain system along the western coast of South America. The Andes, which run through seven countries—Argentina, Chile, Bolivia, Peru, Ecuador, Colombia, and Venezuela—are very tall. The mountain system contains many peaks that exceed 20,000 feet (6,100 meters) in height—that is thirteen times as tall as the world's tallest building. The only mountain range that exceeds the Andes in average elevation is the Himalayas. Some of the highest peaks in the Andes, including Mount Huascarán, are volcanoes (although most are dormant).

WORDS TO KNOW

acid rain: rain that is made more acidic by sulfuric and/or nitric acid in the air, due to the burning of fossil fuels.

Andes: mountain range extending more than 5,000 miles (8,045 kilometers) along the western coast of South America.

Alps: mountain system composed of more than fifteen principle mountain ranges that extends in an arc for almost 660 miles (1,060 kilometers) across south-central Europe.

avalanche path: the course an avalanche takes down a slope, composed of a starting zone, a track, and a runout zone.

avalanche wind: a cloudlike mixture of snow particles and air pushed ahead of a slab avalanche as it races downward.

clear-cutting: the logging practice of harvesting all trees from vast forest tracts.

glacier: slowly flowing masses of ice created by years of snowfall and cold temperatures.

leeward: the side of a mountain facing the direction toward which the wind is blowing (in the United

States, the eastern side). Cold air descends and produces dry conditions on this side.

loose-snow avalanche: avalanche composed of loosely packed snow that begins at a single point and slides down a slope, fanning out in the shape of an inverted V.

plate tectonics: the geologic theory that Earth's crust is composed of rigid plates that float toward or away from each other, either directly or indirectly creating the major geologic features on the planet's surface.

Richter scale: scale that measures the magnitude of an earthquake or size of ground waves generated at the earthquake's source.

slab avalanche: avalanche that begins when fracture lines develop in a snowpack and a large surface plate breaks away, then crumbles into blocks as it falls down a slope.

windward: the side of a mountain facing the direction from which the wind is blowing (in the United States, the western side). Warm air ascends, forms clouds, and yields precipitation on this side.

According to the geological theory known as plate tectonics, the Andes began to form millions of years ago when two plates or sections of Earth's crust advanced toward each other. Upon contact, one plate rode up and over the other, causing the land to rise. To this day, the plates continue to move, and the Andes continue to rise. The continual movement of the plates beneath the Andes makes the area geologically unstable, and earthquakes are common.

The climate in the Andes varies greatly, depending on both altitude (height above sea level) and latitude (distance north or south of the equator measured in degrees). There are hot regions, alpine meadows, glaciers, and a variety of climate types in between. Glaciers form where

Debris from the 1962 Mt. Huascarán avalanche is explored. ©BETTMANN/ CORBIS.

the winter snowfall exceeds the summer snowmelt, such as in high mountainous areas or polar regions.

In the Andes, glaciers occupy about 1,900 square miles (4,921 square kilometers). A section in the Peruvian Andes that has a large number of glaciers is called the White Mountains (*Cordillera Blanca* in Spanish). Named for the ice caps that persist even in the heat of summer, the White Mountains contain dozens of spectacular peaks towering above 19,686 feet (3,000 meters). Mount Huascarán is one of them.

A few years prior to the 1962 disaster, Peruvian geologists had completed a study of the hundreds of glaciers that punctuate the Andes. They had officially labeled the mass of ice atop Mount Huascarán Glacier No. 511. (Since glaciers dot the tops of so many peaks in the White Mountains, geologists assigned them numbers rather than names.)

Glacier no. 511 loomed over a peaceful valley   Glacier No. 511 regularly advanced and retreated with the seasons, creeping forward a few inches each day when fed by winter storms, then retreating slightly during the hot days of summer. Most people living in the valley below the White Mountains simply ignored the glacier—it had always been a part of their landscape. Others relied on the glacier for a source of income. Several Native American families, descendants of the great Inca civilization that had thrived in South America until the Spanish conquest in 1532, regarded the glacier as a type of ice factory. They would scale Mount

*Bodies of Mt. Huascarán
avalanche victims are
identified.* ©BETTMANN/
CORBIS.

Huascarán and chip blocks of ice from the glacier, wrap the ice in grass to prevent it from melting, and carry the blocks on their backs into the villages below. There they would sell the ice to restaurants and stores.

West of the White Mountains is a dark and dry section of the Andes known as the Black Mountains (*Cordillera Negra* in Spanish). Between the White and Black Mountains lies a deep and narrow valley called the Corridor of Greenery (*Callejón de Huailas* in Spanish). This valley, colored by rich green vegetation, is considered by many to be one of the world's most beautiful places. The Santa River (*Rio Santa* in Spanish) flows along the valley floor, framed by tall palm trees whose arching green leaves contrast vividly with the icy white glaciers above. Tourist books refer to this area as the "Switzerland of Peru," since it resembles the Swiss Alps, a section of the great European mountain system renowned for its beauty (and its avalanches as well).

The Corridor of Greenery, lying 750 miles (1,207 kilometers) south of the equator, is located in the Southern Hemisphere. Thus, summer begins in January. At only 9,000 feet (2,743 meters) above sea level—an entire 2.5 miles (4.0 kilometers) below the looming glacier—the valley receives the full effect of the warm equatorial sunshine. Valley residents raise sheep for their wool, and from the wool make handwoven blankets and clothing. They also grow fruit, grain, and vegetables in the fertile land along the Santa River.

The formula behind the disaster Numerous factors tragically combined to send a piece of Glacier No. 511 sliding down the mountain and slamming into the valley below. The glacier had recently grown in thickness due to freak, heavy snowstorms. Several unseasonably hot summer days followed, melting the newly fallen snow. The extreme changes in temperature caused the surface of the glacier to develop cracks, into which flowed melted snow. Increasingly, more surface meltwater flowed downward, creating small streams that seeped to the bottom of the glacier and loosened its hold on the solid rock beneath. The glacier became increasingly unstable.

Geologists do not know for certain which single event forced a massive hunk of the glacier to break off. Some theorize that rocks slid down onto the vulnerable region of the glacier from a rocky peak overhead. Whatever the trigger, at 6:13 PM, as Glacier No. 511 glittered in the setting Sun, an enormous mass of ice broke loose and became the start of a fast-moving, deadly avalanche.

Ripping huge rocks from the cliff face, the falling ice crashed onto a lower section of the glacier 3,000 feet (914 meters) below. The mixture of ice, rock, and snow—preceded by a powdery white cloud—gathered speed as it skidded down the sloped surface of the 2-mile-long (3.2-kilometer-long) glacier. After sliding across the glacier's surface, the speeding ice mass roared into the mouth of the funnel-like valley canyon at more than 65 miles (105 kilometers) per hour.

An eyewitness to the disaster, a man who lived in the nearby city of Yungay, thought he saw a cloud turning golden in the Sun's fading light as he looked at Mount Huascarán. However, he quickly realized, as he told a reporter for *National Geographic* magazine, that "the cloud was flying downhill."

Slamming against the canyon walls, the avalanche cut away house-sized blocks of granite and carried them along in a 150-foot-high (46-meter-high) wall of ice, rock, and mud. The moving mass also kicked up hurricane-strength gusts of wind along its sides. The avalanche's size and momentum

Reports from the past: Ancient avalanches

The Alps, a mountain system extending about 660 miles (1,060 kilometers) across south-central Europe, is renowned for its many glaciers and magnificent scenery. Behind its beauty, however, lies the ever-present threat of avalanches, which have destroyed villages and claimed lives in the region for thousands of years.

Although no written records remain, historians believe many men in the army of Carthaginian general Hannibal (247–183 BCE) died as a result of avalanches. In 218 BCE, during the Second Punic War, Hannibal and his army set out to invade Rome-controlled Italy by crossing the Alps. Historians speculate that during this feat, one of the most remarkable in military history, nearly half of Hannibal's men perished, many smothered by avalanches.

The first written record of avalanches in the Alps appeared nearly two thousand years ago. Greek geographer and historian Strabo (c. 63 BCE–after CE 21) wrote in his *Geographia* that crossing the Alps was dangerous because of ice that fell from the tops of the mountains.

increased as it collected whatever debris lay in its path—topsoil, boulders, even sheep and llamas. Moving swiftly downward, the avalanche created friction along its bottom surface, which in turn melted thousands of tons of ice. The entire mass took on a white, soupy look.

The powerful avalanche scarred the walls of the canyon as it zigzagged downward like a bobsled bouncing against the sides of its track. In a later investigation of the disaster, geologists discovered five separate points of impact where the avalanche had rebounded off the canyon walls. The avalanche gained such force during its descent that it climbed hills as high as 275 feet (84 meters) and even left a 6,000-ton (5,442-metric ton) boulder balanced on top of a ridge.

The thunderous impact of the falling ice was heard and felt by people living in the villages sprinkled throughout the Corridor of Greenery. One person who was at the scene told a *National Geographic* reporter that the sound of the avalanche was a roar "like that of ten thousand beasts."

The first victims   At 6:15 PM, bloated with debris from the canyon floor and walls, the avalanche struck the first of several villages that lay in its path. Pacucco, Yanamachico, and other nearby mountain villages were quickly engulfed. More than eight hundred people were killed; only eight survived. At the moment of impact, the avalanche was twice its original size and traveling at nearly 100 miles (160 kilometers) per hour. Based on the speed and weight of the ice mass, the victims probably died immediately, even before realizing what was happening. Men returning from tending sheep in the fields, women cooking supper, and children playing outdoors were all instantly crushed when the avalanche poured over them.

The avalanche then continued moving toward the more populated region of the valley floor. Fortunately, as the valley became less steep, the speed of the avalanche slowed to about 60 miles (97 kilometers) per hour.

The avalanche remained a lethal force, however, having grown to five times its original size—a volume approximately equal to seven Empire State Buildings. Although a steep bank of land redirected the avalanche away from the city of Yungay, the avalanche raced toward the town of Ranrahirca, with a population of nearly 3,000.

The avalanche struck as the evening lights came on At 6:00 PM, Ranrahirca town electrician Ricardo Olivera had arrived at the town's power station to turn on the electricity for the evening. Mayor Alfonso Caballero stopped by the station to watch the lights come on, then continued his evening walk. Within a few minutes, both men heard the thunder of the approaching avalanche. They raced to their homes to warn their families. Meanwhile, panicked crowds of people jammed the streets. Many townspeople pushed their way toward the church, which they believed would be strong enough to withstand the force of the avalanche. Mayor Caballero safely reached his home, but the oncoming avalanche's roar drowned his shouts of warning to his sister inside. As the electrician Olivera reached his home, he came across two little girls from his neighborhood. Grabbing each one, he tried to pull them to safety on a side street.

Just eight minutes after Olivera had turned on the lights, the avalanche reached Ranrahirca. As the avalanche swept over the town, dust filled the air, choking and blinding the residents. The 40-foot-high (12-meter-high) wall of ice and rock knocked away a corner of Caballero's house, but both the mayor and his sister were spared. Olivera, too, was unharmed, but the edge of the avalanche snatched the two young children from his grasp. They, like members of Olivera's family, were buried beneath tons of ice. The people in the church were also buried as an icy sheet more than twice as tall as the church's steeple overtook them. In the span of just a few moments, between 2,400 and 2,700 people were killed; fewer than 100

Eyewitness report: An English avalanche?

In England, a country noted more for rain than for snow, avalanches are rare—but they do occur. The country's most devastating avalanche struck on December 27, 1836, in the town of Lewes in Sussex, an area in southern England. Heavy snow had begun to fall on the town three days earlier. Meanwhile, strong easterly winds blew back and forth over Cliffe Hill on the outskirts of town. The snow and winds combined to create a cornice or projection of snow that hung over the edge of the hill, some 200 feet (61 meters) above a row of houses below.

The next day residents saw the overhanging snow, but considered it more beautiful than threatening. Two days later, after the warmth of the sun had created a crack in the overhang, one man tried to warn the residents of the impending danger, but they did not listen. That afternoon, the snow cornice broke free and an avalanche buried the houses below, killing eight people.

Afterward, to commemorate the event, a tavern named the Snowdrop Inn was built on the site of the mishap.

people were spared. Most of the survivors lived or worked on the outskirts of the town, beyond the avalanche's route.

The avalanche then spread out like a huge fan on the valley floor. The enormous mass of ice and rock spilled into the Santa River, climbing 100 feet (30 meters) up the opposite bank and creating a dam that produced flood waters more than 15 feet (5 meters) deep. There, at 6:20 PM, nearly 10 miles (16 kilometers) from where it had started, the avalanche stopped. In its wake nearly four thousand people lay dead, most of them buried under the massive pile of ice, mud, and rock. Some bodies were later discovered more than 100 miles (160 kilometers) downstream, where the Santa River empties into the Pacific Ocean.

Relief efforts were futile   Because the avalanche had destroyed telephone and other communication lines in the area, word of the disaster was slow in getting out. Hours passed before government helicopters hovered over the huge stretch of icy white debris, dropping off soldiers to provide help. Medical supplies, doctors, and nurses were transported by airplanes to a small airport in an area untouched by the avalanche. Ranrahirca, which had been a thriving community with cobblestone streets and buildings with red-tiled roofs, lay buried beneath 40 to 60 feet (12 to 18 meters) of mud and rock. There were only about twelve injured people to treat; the rest of the avalanche victims had died. Relief teams quickly realized there was little they could do.

In addition to the great human loss, about ten thousand livestock lay beneath the rocky cover of mud. Rescue workers feared that decomposing animals and human bodies would soon contaminate the region's water supply with disease-carrying germs. Temporary medical clinics were quickly set up to administer vaccinations. Survivors were given shots to protect them against typhoid fever, a deadly disease transmitted by contaminated food or water. To prevent the spread of typhus—another deadly disease typically spread by fleas, lice, or mites—insecticides were sprayed on the remaining trees and plants in the valley.

Two days after the avalanche, U.S. president John F. Kennedy sent a telegram to Peruvian president Manuel Prado y Ugarteche offering the sympathies of all Americans. President Kennedy also asked James Loeb, the U.S. ambassador to Peru, to determine what emergency aid the United States could provide. Unfortunately, since there were so few survivors, there was little assistance any individual or country could offer.

The slow recovery   Fearing that a second avalanche could occur, survivors and rescue workers salvaged belongings and began to clear roads. A refugee center was set up in a high school building that was spared by the avalanche; wooden planks were used to create a temporary footbridge across the wide stretch of muddy rock. Bulldozers were used to clear mud and debris. As the ice melted over the next few weeks, some bodies were unearthed from the mud and, when possible, identified and buried. Since most people were torn to pieces by the powerful impact of the avalanche, the thawing mess became a gruesome scene of scattered body parts.

Local legend suggests that the beautiful mountains around the Corridor of Greenery have hurled down deadly avalanches of ice and snow on past occasions. In fact, in the Native American language Quechua, Ranrahirca means "Hill of Many Stones." Months after the disaster, Mayor Caballero issued a proclamation declaring that a new town of Ranrahirca would someday be built. In honor of the lives lost on that tragic day, the new town's main avenue was to be called the Street of January Tenth.

Recent events: The 1998–99 Swiss avalanche

No country in the world has more of an interest in avalanche research than Switzerland. More than 50 percent of Switzerland's population lives in avalanche terrain. During the 1998–99 avalanche season, the Swiss suffered through their worst avalanche season in forty-five years. Hundreds of major avalanches took place in the Swiss Alps, killing thiry-six people and causing more than $100 million in damages.

The worst of these avalanches took place in the resort town of Evolène in southwest Switzerland, where heavy rain and snowfall triggered an avalanche that killed twelve people. The damage was so severe that the mayor and local security chief were later convicted of failing to take appropriate precautions, such as evacuating houses and closing roads.

Because of its population's vulnerability to avalanches, the Swiss government invests significant resources in the study of avalanches. At the Swiss Federal Institute for Snow and Avalanche Research (the SLF), located in Davos, a small town in eastern Switzerland about 92 miles (147 kilometers) from Zurich, scientists oversee a network of electronic monitors that collect meteorological data that help predict when and where avalanches will take place. Based on this data, the SLF sends out avalanche bulletins advising citizens of avalanche conditions and warning of extreme situations as much as seventy-two hours in advance.

Watch this: "Avalanche!"

In 1997, the PBS program *NOVA* broadcast an episode called "Avalanche!," a look at avalanches and the scientists who study them. According to the show, avalanches are ferocious enough to have earned the nickname "white death." Avalanches are also an increasing problem as skiers, backpackers and snowmobile-riders venture into previously undisturbed back country, where the risk of avalanche is higher.

The show explains the science of avalanches and also follows a team of scientists as they try to learn more about avalanches as they happen. The scientists are so dedicated to understanding and exploring avalanches that at one point in the show an avalanche buries them alive!

Disaster struck once again   A mere eight years after the 1962 disaster, a much larger tragedy befell the Corridor of Greenery. On May 31, 1970, a forty-five-second earthquake with a magnitude of 7.8 on the Richter scale caused a huge amount of rock and glacial ice to break off the west face of Mount Huascarán and plummet down toward the valley. Within three minutes, almost 80 million cubic yards (61 million cubic meters) of ice, rock, water, and debris traveled nearly 11 miles (18 kilometers). Traveling at an average speed of 100 miles (160 kilometers) per hour, the avalanche completely buried the city of Yungay (spared in 1962) and nearly a dozen villages, killing almost 20,000 people in the Corridor of Greenery. (Overall, the earthquake claimed a total of 70,000 lives across an area of about 32,370 square miles [83,000 square kilometers].)

Dangerous science: What causes avalanches?

While any movement of snow, ice, rocks, or mud down the slope of a mountain or hill can be considered an avalanche, the term is most often used to describe the rapid downward movement of a vast quantity of snow. (The movement of rocks and mud is more commonly known as a landslide.) Scientists estimate that as many as one million avalanches take place around the world each year. Of these, most occur in the Alps in Austria, France, Italy, and Switzerland. In the mountainous western region of the United States, approximately 100,000 avalanches tumble down each year (most of them are in the Rocky Mountains). The number of avalanches in the United States is small in comparison to the number in the Alps and the Andes.

Snow avalanches take on many forms but are generally placed into two categories: loose-snow and slab. Slab avalanches are, by far, the more common and more deadly of the two.

Loose-snow avalanches   A loose-snow avalanche (also called a pure avalanche) is, as its name implies, composed of snowflakes or snow crystals that are loosely packed. The crystals behave much like dry sand:

the bonds between them are not very strong, and they merely lie upon each other. A loose-snow avalanche usually begins at a single point on a slope when a small portion of snow slips and begins to slide, knocking into other crystals on the surface. As the avalanche runs downward, picking up more snow, it fans out in the shape of an inverted V.

If the snow on the slope is dry and powdery, the loose-snow avalanche can travel at speeds up to 100 miles (160 kilometers) per hour. Conversely, if the snow involved is melting and wet, the avalanche may move at speeds of only 5 to 10 miles (8 to 16 kilometers) per hour. Some loose-snow avalanches travel only 10 to 30 feet (16 to 48 meters) before stopping.

Unstable snow is the most significant factor in the creation of a loose-snow avalanche, as it is in a slab avalanche. Where snow is loosely packed on a slope, any disturbance of the delicate balance existing near the slope's surface will result in a slide. The added weight of new snow dropped by a fierce storm is a leading cause. Additional snow

An avalanche in the Karakoram Mountains in Pakistan. ©GALEN ROWELL/ CORBIS.

can also be deposited on a slope by winds, which usually blow up one side of a hill or mountain (called the windward side) and down the other (called the leeward side). As winds blow up the windward side, they scrape loose snow from the slope and drop it on the leeward side after passing over the summit. This accumulation of snow stresses the existing snowpack, causing it to slide. Another strain on a snowpack can be brought about by the warmth of the Sun, which melts snow at the surface, making it denser and heavier.

Slab avalanches   A slab avalanche begins when fracture lines develop in the snowpack and a large surface plate breaks away and then crumbles into blocks as it falls down a slope. As with a loose-snow avalanche, many factors combine to produce a slab avalanche—including the condition of the snowpack, temperature, weather, and wind direction. Unlike a loose-snow avalanche, a slab avalanche brings down large amounts of snow all at once, making it much more powerful and dangerous. A slab may be more

Loose-snow avalanche.

than 100,000 square feet (9,290 square meters) in area (equal to three 100-unit apartment buildings) and more than 30 feet (9 meters) thick. As it tumbles down the slope at speeds approaching 100 miles (160 kilometers) per hour or greater, it picks up more snow and may grow to one hundred times its original size.

Again, unstable snow is the main trigger behind a slab avalanche. Throughout a winter season, numerous layers of snow build up on a slope. As layers of snow are deposited during storms, the snow crystals making up the existing layers are compacted by the weight of new snow. The older crystals become rounded, generally forming stronger bonds between themselves and making the snow layer more stable. Under optimum conditions, the weather and temperature during and between storms remain the same. Consistently cold temperatures and light snows allow each new layer to bond readily and tightly to the layer just beneath the surface.

Slab avalanche.

Weather and temperature on a mountain slope, however, hardly ever remain the same, even within a single day. Clear, warm spells often abruptly change to stormy ones. These large variations in temperature and snowfall create unstable snow layers. If cold nights follow warm days, then the crystals within a snowpack melt and refreeze, weakening the bonds between them. If warm days follow a snowfall, then the crystals in the upper layer may melt and form a slick surface to which subsequent snowfalls do not easily bond. Rain also creates slick surfaces, not only on the top layer but throughout the lower layers in a snowpack.

Snowfall and wind direction can also contribute to the creation of a slab avalanche. The added weight of a single snowfall measuring 12 inches (30 centimeters) or more can quickly produce an extremely destructive avalanche. Winds blowing up the windward side of a mountain deposit snow unevenly on the leeward side to create unstable conditions.

Earthquakes and even minor earth tremors can also set off a slab avalanche. As the ground beneath a slope moves, fractures may develop in an unstable snowpack and a large section may break loose.

Both slab and loose-snow avalanches can occur on any slope, but they most often take place on slopes that have angles measuring between 30° and 45°. Snow on slopes with angles less than 30° is generally more stable and not affected as much by the pull of gravity. Snow on slopes with angles more than 45° generally does not have a chance to accumulate because it sloughs (pronounced SLUFFS) off in frequent little avalanches.

Aftermath: The effects of avalanches

Loose-snow avalanches are usually not dangerous, but there are exceptions. Large loose-snow avalanches can carry humans and animals over the edge of a cliff or bury them in deep snow. They can also destroy buildings and whole sections of forest. Even worse, on a very unstable slope, a fast-moving loose-snow avalanche can trigger a larger slab avalanche.

Slab avalanches, because of their great size, are almost always dangerous. A large slab avalanche will usually mow down and carry away anything in its path: trees, boulders, animals, humans, and buildings. Slab avalanches composed of powdery snow have an additional destructive aspect—avalanche wind. As an avalanche sweeps down a slope, wind rushes ahead of the sliding snow mass. This wind, a mixture of snow particles and air around the avalanche, is like a dust cloud or a heavy gas and is difficult to breathe. When the avalanche comes to a sudden stop, the wind around it rushes out violently in all directions. The force of this wind is especially destructive if the sliding snow or ice mass has fallen almost vertically to a valley floor. Like a bomb blast, the wind can actually blow down nearby houses and other structures.

Avalanche paths   The course an avalanche takes down a slope is called the avalanche path. Large avalanches traveling repeatedly down the same path leave a lasting scar on Earth's surface. Such scars appear as bare lines on a mountainside otherwise covered with trees and vegetation.

Paths can run through narrow gullies or across open slopes. Although they differ in shape and length, avalanche paths all have three main parts: the starting zone, the track, and the runout zone. The starting zone is where the avalanche begins, typically high up on a slope. At the starting zone, snow collects unevenly; loose surface snow begins to slough, or fracture lines cut slabs from the snowpack. The track is the trail or channel the avalanche takes

Eyewitness report: The Wellington disaster

The worst avalanche disaster in the United States occurred at Wellington, Washington, in 1910. Wellington was a small railroad town consisting of a railroad depot, a few railroad sheds and bunkhouses, and a hotel. It was located at the western end of the Cascade Tunnel, which runs almost 8 miles (13 kilometers) through the Cascade Mountain Range.

Two trains, a mail train and a passenger train of seven cars, came to a halt on the westbound tracks at Wellington in the late evening of February 24, 1910. Heavy snow had been falling for days, and portions of the track ahead of the trains lay buried under snowdrifts and small avalanches. Looming above the trains was the broad, snow-covered slope of Windy Mountain.

For days after, the trains were motionless as railroad workers tried to clear the tracks with rotary plows. Progress was slow. While the plows were clearing packed snow in one area, snow would pile up in another area. One plow soon broke down and another, out of fuel, was stranded between snow piles.

Railroad workers, discovering that the telegraph lines were down, decided to hike 4 miles (6 kilometers) through the snow to the depot of Scenic to send for more plows and men. Shortly thereafter, six male passengers and a few more railroad men joined them. The remaining passengers and railroad laborers remained with the trains, waiting for the weather to change.

During the evening of February 28, the falling snow turned to rain, and a lightning storm followed. At 1:30 AM on March 1, a snow mass about 1,350 feet (411 meters) wide slipped loose from the slope of Windy Mountain and dropped 500 feet (152 meters) to the tracks below. The avalanche carried the passenger train, the mail train, a plow, some boxcars and electric engines, and more than 100 people over a ledge and into a canyon 150 feet (46 meters) below.

Railroad workers who had not been on the trains quickly descended into the canyon and began digging for survivors. The digging, slow and by hand, continued for eight days. When it was complete, only 22 of the 118 passengers and workers who had been buried by the avalanche had been found alive.

as it races downward. This middle section of the track is where the rushing snow or ice mass reaches its greatest speed. The runout zone is where the snow and debris finally come to a halt. It may be a level area at the base of a mountain where the avalanche gradually slows down, or a deep gully or ravine where the avalanche stops abruptly. The runout zone, where snow and debris pile the highest, is where victims are most often buried.

Avalanches and the paths they create do have certain benefits. Since trees and other large plants have been cleared from these paths, meadows are able to develop in spring and summer. Filled with grasses, wildflowers, and small shrubs, these areas provide necessary food for mountain-dwelling animals such as bear, deer, elk, and moose.

Avalanches have little, if any, benefits for humans. Any interaction between avalanches and humans typically ends in destruction, injury, and death. Roads and towns built near avalanche paths are either partially or completely buried. Each year, thousands of people around the world are killed or injured in avalanches.

The human factor

For thousands of years, humans have settled in valleys at the base of mountains where snow runs down and forms clear streams, and the fertile soil produces abundant vegetation. The natural beauty of such settings is often astounding. As long as humans have inhabited these areas, however, they have had to face the peril of avalanches. For centuries, villages in the Swiss Alps have been buried by avalanches, only to be rebuilt and buried again.

Forests surrounding these valley communities have provided protection against the force of certain avalanches: trees in mature or well-developed forests can slow or stop the rush of a small avalanche. But over time, as these villages grew in size, the inhabitants began to cut down the surrounding trees for fuel and housing. In the process, they destroyed their only protective barrier. In modern times, remaining forest regions in the Alps have withered away because of the effects of acid rain (rain that is made more acidic by sulfuric and/or nitric acid in the air, due to the burning of fossil fuels). In the western United States, the risk of avalanche damage has increased because of the clear-cutting of forests (logging practice of harvesting all trees from vast forest tracts).

Avalanche fatalities have also recently increased because of an upsurge in mountain recreation activities. In the United States and other countries, thousands of people are drawn each year to mountain areas to ski, hike, and take part in other winter sports. To accommodate these recreationists, roads, buildings, and towns have been built in avalanche-prone areas, increasing the risk of avalanche-related deaths.

With increasing numbers of people entering hazardous mountain terrain, more and more avalanches are being triggered. Larger avalanches are usually set off by natural events and do not involve people unless they happen to be in the area. Small- and medium-sized avalanches are responsible for more human deaths overall because humans often set them off. In the United States, snowmobilers, climbers, and backcountry skiers are the parties most responsible for starting avalanches. The simple weight of these people on unstable snow is enough to begin an avalanche that, most times,

Two avalanches simultaneously make their way through a ski resort in the Swiss Alps. © FABRICE COFFRINI/EPA/CORBIS.

kills them. Experts predict that as the sport of snowboarding increases in popularity, snowboarders will join the list of victims.

A matter of survival: Living through avalanches Nearly all avalanche fatalities can be avoided. Two ways to accomplish that are to stop building communities in avalanche-prone mountain valleys and to prohibit recreation on mountain slopes. Both solutions, however, are impractical.

In areas where avalanches frequently threaten communities, numerous steps can be taken to lessen their impact. On the slopes above roads or buildings, structures may be erected to either prevent avalanches from starting or to divert the path of an avalanche. Planting trees close together, for instance, can help prevent the formation of avalanches and stop the approach of ones that do develop. In starting zones, areas higher up on slopes where trees will usually not grow, large fences can be erected to

Examples of various structures built to lessen the impact of avalanches.

keep the snow from sliding down. Large, slotted barriers called snow rakes can also be used to decrease the amount and speed of the falling snow mass.

Farther down the avalanche path, where roads or railroad tracks pass through, avalanche sheds can be built. A shed, constructed like an overpass with one end built into the slope, diverts the snow over the road or tracks to fall on the other side. Near buildings or other structures, heavy stone or concrete walls can be built to deflect the snow. In the lower reaches of an avalanche path, earth or rock mounds can also be constructed to break up the snow mass and slow its speed.

An interesting design that provides direct protection to buildings is a wedge-shaped wall built in front of the structure with its point facing the slope. Sometimes, the building's wall that faces the slope is itself constructed in the shape of a wedge. Much like a ship's bow that cuts through water, the wedge-shaped wall cuts into the oncoming snow mass, forcing it to travel around the sides of the building.

In areas where roads and railroad tracks follow mountainous terrain for miles, the cost of these protective measures is prohibitive. In such situations, avalanche experts periodically use explosives—shot by cannon or gun, dropped from helicopters, or placed by hand—to dislodge the snow. This creates small avalanches and thus prevents the accumulation of heavier, and possibly more destructive, snowpacks.

Avalanche barriers on Mannlichen Mountain, Switzerland. ©NICK HAWKES; ECOSCENE/CORBIS.

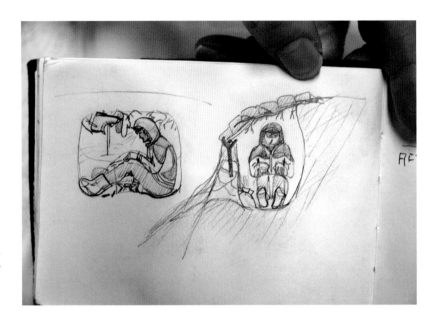

A Dutch youth shows a drawing of how he survived being buried in an avalanche in northern Norway. ©EPA/CORBIS.

Personal safety   For those venturing onto mountains, there are a few steps to avoid becoming a victim of an avalanche. The most critical step is to gather as much information in advance about snowpack conditions and upcoming weather from forest service, national park, or ski patrol personnel. Before going on a mountain, it is also wise to have proper safety equipment, including an avalanche transceiver or beacon (a device that emits a signal indicating one's position) and a portable shovel. In addition, when on a mountainside, it is important to be alert to the surrounding conditions, such as the slope angle, tender or weak spots in the snow, fracture lines and other disruptions on the surface, and wind direction. When traveling on a snowy mountain, it is also safest to be part of a group. If buried by an avalanche, an individual will most likely need the help of others to get out alive.

People caught in an avalanche die in one of two ways: they either suffer a fatal injury when they hit a boulder or tree during the slide, or they suffocate to death shortly after the slide comes to a halt. If caught in an avalanche, one's chances of survival are increased if certain techniques are followed. When the avalanche begins to slide, try to get out of its path or even move to its sides, where the snow will be moving more slowly. Remove any packs, skis, snowshoes, ski poles, or any other baggage that might weigh one down. If possible, grab a tree, large boulder, or something solid before the avalanche picks up speed. During the slide, try to stay near the snow's surface by "swimming" through the snow mass. When the slide begins to

Eyewitness report: The Iceman appears

On September 19, 1991, a German tourist set out walking across a glacier in the Alps between Austria and Italy. That summer and previous winter had both been warm. Warm winds had also been plentiful in the region. As a result, glaciers in the area had been melting; as they did, they revealed bodies of victims of climbing accidents from years past. Already that year Italian authorities had extracted eight bodies from the glaciers.

It wasn't a total surprise, then, when the tourist came upon the head and shoulders of a man frozen in the ice. Seeing a hole in the back of the man's head, the tourist suspected he had been the victim of a murder and so notified the police. When the dead man's body was removed from the ice, however, it was evident that he had been dead for an extremely long time. While the bodies of most victims trapped in a glacier are white and waxy, the body of this victim was brown and dried out.

Scientists were called in to determine the age of the dead man. After performing radiocarbon dating tests (a method of measuring the amount of carbon 14 left in organic matter), the scientists concluded the man in the ice was at least 5,200 years old. Dubbed the Iceman, he was the oldest human being ever discovered whose body was virtually intact.

Scientists speculated that the Iceman had been a shepherd who was caught in a storm and froze to death. Either icy winds or foehns dried out his body before it was covered by heavy snowfall or, more likely, an avalanche. Over time, the heavy snow compacted into ice and the Iceman's body was preserved by the cold temperature (about 21°F [–6°C]). The Iceman remained hidden for fifty-three centuries before the warm seasons and the dry winds uncovered him.

The Iceman, nicknamed "Otzi," was found with several of his belongings, including a backpack, axe, dagger, and bow and arrows. ©CORBIS/CORBIS SYGMA.

Reports from the past: Avalanche casualties in World War I

World War I (1914–18) is known as the Great War because it was the largest war up to that time. In addition to the men killed by weapons, many died from natural occurrences such as disease and avalanches. It is believed that between forty thousand and eighty thousand men were victims of avalanches during the conflict.

Experts estimate that in the Dolomites, a section of the Alps in northern Italy, more men died in avalanches than from bullets, shells, and other weapons of war. During the early winter of 1916, the region received more snow than it had in fifty years. A warm period in December thawed the snow, and on December 13, more than one hundred avalanches plunged down the valleys in the Dolomites. Almost ten thousand Austrian and Italian troops were killed on that single day. Their bodies were still being recovered over thirty-five years later.

slow down, move around as much as possible. It is important to create a large breathing space rapidly, for within seconds after the snow stops moving it will harden.

Once trapped, a person may not know in what direction the surface lies. An easy way to find out is to spit or drool. The surface will be the opposite direction that the saliva flows. If a person is near the surface, he or she may be able to dig through the snow and stick a hand out to be visible to rescuers. If this is not possible, a person should remain calm—it is very important not to waste energy or remaining air by struggling. If one's avalanche beacon is in the transmit mode—and it should have been from the time he or she stepped onto the mountain—then searchers will have a better chance for a successful rescue.

Finding survivors or victims   Survivors of avalanches are most often found within the first thirty minutes after an avalanche comes to a stop. Group members who have not been buried are the ones who make the most rescues. They do so by honing in on the buried person's beacon signal with their own transceiver; by finding a glove, hat, or other sign that the person might be near the surface; by using metal probes; or by remembering where that person was last seen and then checking downhill from there.

The longer it takes to find a buried person, the less chance that person will survive. By the time most rescue teams arrive, the chance of finding any survivors is very slim.

Professional rescuers use a combination of equipment (such as sonar, radar, and infrared detectors) and trained dogs to find buried people. An avalanche dog, relying on its keen sense of smell, can search an area of more than 1,000 square feet (93 square meters) in less than thirty minutes. A team of twenty people searching the same area would need four hours. By then, anyone who was buried would almost certainly be dead.

Technology connection: Measuring and predicting avalanches

Unfortunately, scientists cannot accurately predict exactly when and where an avalanche will take place. They can determine, however, when conditions exist that are favorable for an avalanche to occur.

Avalanche experts first look at the layers within a snowpack to decide if the snow in that area might slide. They start by digging what is called a snow pit. Dug deep into a snowpack, the snow pit reveals the composition of the layers of that snowpack. After digging, the avalanche testers use shovels to probe the various layers and determine if they differ in hardness. The crystals in the layers are examined to see if a layer of powdery, loosely packed snow is lying underneath a layer of wet, denser snow. The depth of the snowpack and the angle of the slope on which it lies is also checked.

Having gathered this information, avalanche professionals monitor the weather forecast. Is a low-pressure system moving into the area, bringing with it colder temperatures and snowstorms? Or is a warm front forecasted, which may cause surface melting? Finally, they check previous data to see if a particular area is prone to avalanches and if so, what time of year they typically happen. (Most avalanche fatalities in the United States occur in February.)

Around the world, many avalanche-prone regions have prediction services. The Swiss Federal Snow Institute for Snow and Avalanche Research, founded in 1936 in Switzerland, has about seventy observation stations located in the Alps at altitudes of 3,280 to 5,905 feet (1,000 to 1,800 meters). Observers in these stations record information about snow conditions, then transmit it to the institute. There the information is processed and, if necessary, avalanche warnings are issued to newspapers and radio and television stations. In the United States avalanche danger is monitored mainly by the U.S. Forest Service, since most ski areas are located within national forests. In addition, various western states prone to avalanches hire avalanche professionals to provide prediction services.

[*See Also* **Earthquake; Landslide**]

For More Information

BOOKS

Drohan, Michele Ingber. *Avalanches.* New York: Rosen Publishing Group, 1998.

Ferguson, Sue, and Edward R. LaChapelle. *The ABCs of Avalanche Safety.* 3rd ed., Seattle, WA: Mountaineers Books, 2003.

Hamilton, Richard. *Avalanches: Nature's Fury.* Minneapolis, MN: Abdo and Daughters, 2005.

Merrick, Patrick. *Avalanches.* Plymouth, MN: Child's World, 1998.

WEB SITES

American Avalanche Association. <http://www.americanavalancheassociation.org/> (accessed August 17, 2006).

"Avalanche!" *NOVA Online.* <http://www.pbs.org/wgbh/nova/avalanche/> (accessed August 17, 2006).

Avalanche Awareness. *National Snow and Ice Data Center.* <http://nsidc.org/snow/avalanche/> (accessed August 17, 2006).

National Avalanche Center. *U.S. Forest Service.* <http://www.avalanche.org/%7enac/> (accessed August 17, 2006).

Blizzard

A blizzard is a severe winter storm characterized by strong winds and blowing snow. The National Weather Service defines a blizzard as a large amount of falling or blowing snow with winds greater than 35 miles (56 kilometers) per hour and visibility reduced to 0.25 mile (0.4 kilometer) for at least three hours. A severe blizzard is defined as having wind speeds in excess of 45 miles (72 kilometers) per hour with temperatures of 10°F (–12°C) or lower.

Most blizzards are accompanied by heavy snowfalls and temperatures of 20°F (–6°C) or lower. The falling and blowing of fine, powdery snow during a blizzard sometimes reduces visibility to less than a few yards (meters).

Blizzards create conditions that are dangerous for motorists and pedestrians. Commerce and transportation systems typically grind to a halt and roofs may collapse under the weight of the snow. Many lives are lost in blizzards due to hypothermia, a drastic drop in body temperature; frostbite, a freezing of the skin; or overexertion while shoveling snow.

Blizzards occur mainly in Canada, the United States, Russia, and the former Soviet Republics, central and northern Europe, and central and northern Asia. The United States usually experiences one to seven blizzards per year, although some winters have recorded as many as thirty-five. Blizzards occur in the United States primarily during the months of December through March.

The blizzard of 1888

From March 10 through 14, 1888, a blizzard besieged the East Coast of the United States and set snowfall records from Virginia to Maine. The Blizzard of '88—with its combination of heavy snowfall, whipping winds, and frigid temperatures—was the most devastating weather event in the history of the northeastern United States. Throughout southern New England and southeastern New York, snowfalls averaged

WORDS TO KNOW

air mass: a large quantity of air—measuring thousands of square miles (the size of several states) across—where temperature and moisture content are fairly constant throughout.

blizzard: the most severe type of winter storm, characterized by winds of 35 miles (56 kilometers) per hour or greater, large quantities of falling or blowing snow, and low temperatures.

frostbite: the freezing of the skin.

ground blizzard: the drifting and blowing of snow that occurs after a snowfall has ended.

heavy snow: snowfall that reduces visibility to 0.31 mile (0.5 kilometer) and yields, on average, 4 inches (10 centimeters) or more in a twelve-hour period or 6 inches (15 centimeters) or more in a twenty-four-hour period.

hollow column: a snowflake in the shape of a long, six-sided column.

hypothermia: a condition characterized by a drop in core body temperature from the normal 98.6°F (37°C) to 95°F (35°C) or lower.

nor'easter: a strong, northeasterly wind that brings cold air, often accompanied by heavy rain, snow, or sleet, to the coastal areas of New England and the mid-Atlantic states. Also called northeaster.

sector plate: a star-shaped snowflake.

severe blizzard: a blizzard in which wind speeds exceed 45 miles (72 kilometers) per hour, snowfall is heavy, and the temperature is 10°F (−12°C) or lower.

stratus: gloomy, gray, featureless sheets of clouds that cover the entire sky, at low levels of the atmosphere.

whiteout: a condition in which falling, drifting, and blowing snow reduces visibility to almost zero.

windchill factor: the cooling effect on the body due to a combination of wind and temperature.

40 inches (100 centimeters) or more and winds were recorded at 50 to 80 miles (80 to 128 kilometers) per hour. Temperatures hovered near 0°F (−18°C).

New York City, Washington, D.C., Philadelphia, and Boston—the nation's economic and political centers—were all paralyzed by the storm. Two hundred ships in coastal waters were run aground, and many of them were destroyed by winds of 60 to 75 miles (97 to 121 kilometers) per hour. Four hundred people on city streets, in the countryside, and aboard ships perished in the blizzard because of exposure to strong winds and low temperatures. Half of the fatalities were in New York City. Thousands of people were stricken with frostbite and exhaustion.

Snow piled in front of a New York store in 1888. ©BETT-MANN/CORBIS.

Blizzard caused by convergence of storms   The intensity of the blizzard was the result of the convergence of two low-pressure systems: one, a warm, moist air mass from the south, and the other a storm system from the west. A low-pressure system is a region of low air pressure measuring thousands of square miles in area, the size of several states, that brings clouds and sometimes stormy conditions.

The southern air mass originated on March 9 over the northern Gulf of Mexico. During the next couple of days it traveled to the northeast, through Georgia and North Carolina, to New England. On March 11 and 12, the air mass held a steady position over the coast of southern New England. At the same time, a cold northeasterly wind, called a nor'easter, blew cold air into the region.

The western low-pressure system developed on March 8 over Salt Lake City, Utah. Over the next two days it moved across Colorado and the Missouri River Valley and on to the Great Lakes region. The western system ran into the southern system over Cape Hatteras, North Carolina, and formed a monstrous storm system. The storm then headed up the coast toward New York City at 80 miles (129 kilometers) per hour.

New York City gets 22 inches of snow   By daybreak on March 12, snowdrifts several feet high made the streets impassable. Visibility was reduced to a few hundred feet. By that afternoon, no trains were entering or leaving New York City. The winds were strong enough to knock people off their feet and tip streetcars off their tracks. The pedestrian bridges into Manhattan were also closed. Several hundred determined people, however, walked between Manhattan and Long Island across a pack of ice that had floated up the East River and became trapped between the two shores.

On the morning of Tuesday, March 13, the temperature was –1°F (–18°C), and the snow was still falling. Several small fires broke out as the result of faulty heating stoves. Fortunately, firefighters were able to extinguish the blazes before they developed into major fires.

By the time the snow quit early on March 14, snowfall in New York City measured 22 inches (56 centimeters), Brooklyn was socked with 26 inches (66 centimeters), and White Plains had 32 inches (81 centimeters) on the ground. The wind continued blowing even after the snow stopped, whipping up enormous drifts.

The damage in New York City   The snowfall in New York City brought power lines to the ground and disabled the city's new telephone and electrical systems. Four workers with the New York and Harlem Railroad were killed when they tried to crash their train through a huge snowdrift. Many horses perished, buried in snowdrifts. March 12 went down in the history books as being the first weekday the New York Stock Exchange closed since its opening in 1790.

The blizzard paralyzes the region   The blizzard socked New Jersey, eastern New York, Connecticut, Vermont, New Hampshire, and other parts of New England, as well as the cities of Boston and Philadelphia. Railroad service was cut off. In parts of upstate New York, Connecticut, and western Massachusetts, 40 to 50 inches (102 to 127 centimeters) of snow fell, and drifts measured 30 to 40 feet (9 to 12 meters). In Middletown, New York, where the snow reached the second stories of buildings, residents dug tunnels across streets. In Pittsfield, Massachusetts, some houses on the main thoroughfare were entirely buried by 20 feet (6 meters) of snow.

Albany and Troy, in northeastern New York state, each received more than 4 feet of snow in just a few hours—as did Middleton, Connecticut. The site of the largest snowfall was Saratoga Springs, New York, with 58 inches (147 centimeters). Gravesend, New York, had a snowdrift of 52 feet (15.6 meters), only topped by New Haven, Connecticut's 53-foot (16-meter) snowdrift.

In Camden, New Jersey, residents were trapped in their homes by mountains of snow. Ferry service to Philadelphia was hampered by severe winds, which blew the water right out of the Delaware River. The water level was driven so low in parts of the river that loaded ferries scraped bottom. One boat full of passengers struck ground and became stranded midway across the channel.

Recent events: Catastrophic blizzards

In recent years the northeastern United States has been hit hard by winter storms. The years between 2000 and 2005 saw three record-breaking storms that were both damaging and deadly.

Poles fall down after the blizzard of 1888. © CORBIS-BETTMANN.

In 2003 the northeastern United States saw an historic blizzard. The Blizzard of 2003, which is also called the President's Day Blizzard, caused then-record snowfalls across the region. The storm caused over 40 inches of snow to fall in Garrett County, Maryland, and almost as much in parts of West Virginia.

The President's Day Blizzard of 2003 exacted a greater human toll than some major storms in the following years. The 2003 storm caused at least forty-four deaths. The effort to clean up and repair damages caused by the storm cost tens of millions of dollars.

January 2005 brought another powerful winter storm to the northeastern United States. The 2005 blizzard was one of the worst storms on record to hit the region. Heavy snows covered the eastern seaboard from Mississippi to New England. At the height of the storm, as much as three feet of snow blanketed parts of Massachusetts, which saw some of the worst of the storm.

The National Weather Service ranked the Blizzard of 2005 in the top five storms in the past 100 years. The service compared the blizzard to the catastrophic Blizzard of 1978, which caused $1 billion in damage. The

Snowplows clear snow during a blizzard in Rhode Island. AP IMAGES.

temperature in Boston during the storm came within one degree of the record set by the historic Blizzard of 1888. Temperatures during that storm were logged at −2°F (−18°C).

Despite the severity of the storm, the Blizzard of 2005 did not cause the type of casualties and havoc wrought by earlier storms, like the Blizzard of 1978. This is partly due to advances in technology and forecasting, which allowed preparations for the storm to be made.

In 2006, just more than a year after the Blizzard of 2005, another powerful storm hit the northeastern and mid-Atlantic regions of the United States. The storm caused record amounts of snow accumulation. This severe storm lasted from February 11 though 13. The 2006 blizzard dumped at least a foot of snow on mid-Atlantic and northeastern U.S. cities. However, despite record amounts of snow, the storm caused relatively few casualties.

Snow accumulations for the 2006 blizzard broke records. Snowfall in Central Park in New York City was recorded at 26.9 inches, an all-time record for the city. By contrast, the destructive and famous Blizzard of 1888 caused only 22 inches of snow in the city. The 2006 blizzard caused well more than 25 inches of snow throughout Connecticut and New Jersey. The storm's low-pressure system deepened as it moved up the eastern seaboard, causing power outages in tens of thousands of homes.

Dangerous science: How blizzards happen

Blizzards form in winter when two or more air masses of different temperatures and different air pressures collide. One of the air masses must contain warm, moist air, and the other cold, arctic air. For blizzards that occur in the United States, the warm air mass comes from the southern states or the Gulf of Mexico, and the cold air mass comes from Canada.

When a cold air mass advances upon a warm air mass, the approaching cold air is called a cold front. When this happens, the cold air, being denser and heavier than the warm air, wedges underneath the warm air and forces it sharply upward. The infusion of cold air causes the temperature on the ground to drop sharply. The collision of air masses also produces strong winds because of the difference in air pressures between the two masses.

The warm air cools as it rises, and water vapor within it condenses and forms clouds. Those clouds may take the form of a low-lying layer, called stratus, or they may develop steeply upward into thunderstorm clouds.

If the temperature in the clouds drops below freezing, ice crystals form. Ice crystals can then grow into snowflakes by several methods. When the snowflakes become too heavy to remain suspended in the cloud, they fall to the ground. The combination of sudden cold temperatures, high winds, and snow results in a blizzard.

Consequences of blizzards

When a blizzard strikes, it spells danger for motorists, pedestrians, public transportation systems, communication systems, and buildings. Blizzards frequently cause auto accidents, force traffic to a standstill, strand motorists, knock out power, freeze pipes, and shut down entire cities. Airports and railroads close because travel becomes too dangerous. A blizzard's whipping winds can create snowdrifts tall enough to bury cars or even buildings. A blizzard's heavy snows can make roofs collapse. Blizzards can cause agricultural losses by killing livestock and destroying crops.

Blizzards can also claim human lives. Seven out of ten people who die in blizzards are trapped in their cars and succumb to hypothermia, which is a drastic reduction of body temperature. Others die in traffic accidents on snowy, low-visibility roads. Some motorists trapped in blizzards become unconscious or die because of dangerous fumes that enter their running car when the car's tailpipe becomes clogged with snow.

When falling, drifting, and blowing snow reduces visibility to almost zero, the condition is called a whiteout. Everything appears white, making the ground and sky indistinguishable. In such conditions, a stranded person may become disoriented and lose their way. People in whiteouts

A key reference to: The structure of snowflakes

While snowflakes come in a variety of shapes, they all have the same basic hexagonal (six-sided) configuration. The structure of ice crystals, the smallest units of snowflakes, is also hexagonal. This basic shape can be traced back to water molecules. Because of the electrical attraction between water molecules, they form a hexagon when they freeze.

A snowflake begins its existence as an ice crystal within a cold cloud, where ice crystals coexist with water droplets that are supercooled— meaning they remain in the liquid state below the freezing point. As an ice crystal is bounced between the bottom and top of the cloud by the wind and by currents within the cloud caused by differences in temperature, the crystal grows. This can be the result of coalescence, in which the crystal hits and sticks to supercooled water drops, or by deposition, in which water vapor molecules in the cloud freeze and stick directly onto the ice crystal. As the ice crystal grows, it bonds with other ice crystals and takes on the shape of a snowflake. When the snowflake becomes heavy enough, it falls to the ground.

Snowflakes can exist in the following forms: flat, hexagonal plates; long, six-sided columns; needles that are two hundred times longer than they are wide, or starry shapes called sector plates. When a sector plate accumulates moisture it may develop feathery branches on its arms, thus becoming a dendrite—the most distinctive and most common type of snowflake. As dendrites bounce around through a cloud they may combine with other dendrites, forming a variety of complex patterns.

The shape of a snowflake depends upon the air temperature in which it is formed. Hollow columns, for instance, form when the temperature is either below −8°F (−22°C) or between 14 and 21°F (−10 and −6°C). Sector plates form at temperatures between −8 and 3°F (−22 and −16°C) and between 10 and 14°F (−12 and −10°C). When the temperature is between 3 and 10°F (−16 and −12°C), dendrites are formed. Between 21 and 25°F (−6 and −4°C) you get needles, and over 25°F (−4°C) you get thin, hexagonal plates.

The size of a snowflake depends upon the temperature of the air as the snowflake descends. If the temperature is above freezing, the snowflake melts around the edges. This process produces a

have frozen to death just steps from their door. People have even choked to death on the blowing fine, powdery snow. Other causes of death during blizzards are frostbite and heart attacks.

Cold weather is hard on humans   Low air temperatures combine with high winds during blizzards to produce the wind chill factor: the *apparent* temperature, or how cold it feels. For instance, when it is 0°F (−18°C) outside and the wind is blowing at 20 miles (32 kilometers) per hour, it feels like −40°F (−40°C). In low wind chills, humans are susceptible to hypothermia, which is the drop in the internal body temperature from film of water, which acts like glue. Snowflakes that strike each other stick together, producing large, soggy snowflakes, 2 to 4 inches (5 to 10 centimeters) or greater in diameter. These snowflakes stick to surfaces and are heavy to shovel.

Snowflakes that descend into cold, dry air, in contrast, do not readily combine with one another. Those flakes produce dry, powdery snow on the ground that is ideal for skiing.

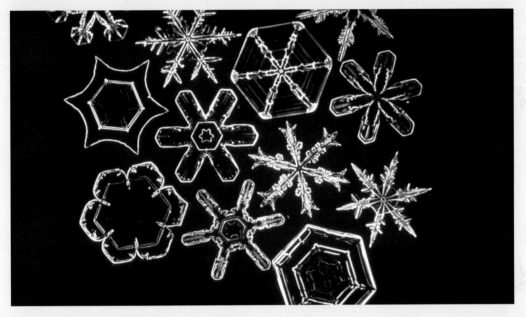

Electron microscopy shows many different snowflake shapes. ©ELIZABETH SAUER/ZEFA/CORBIS.

the normal 98.6°F (37°C) down to 95°F (35°C) or lower, as well as to frostbite, which is the freezing of the skin.

The human body has little natural protection against the cold. Without the proper clothing in cold weather, a person rapidly loses body heat. Even at 68°F (20°C), an unclothed person will begin to shiver. Children and older people are the least able to withstand cold weather since their bodies regulate temperature with less efficiency than people of other age groups.

Once hypothermia sets in, a person will shiver violently and experience a gradual loss of physical and mental functions. As the body

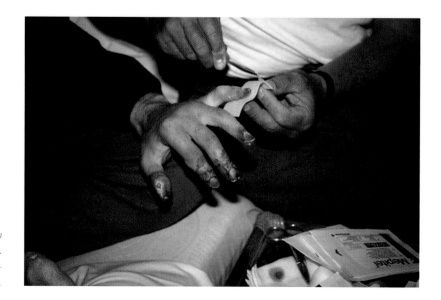

A doctor treats the frostbitten hand of a mountain climber.
©JASON BURKE; EYE UBIQUI-
TOUS/CORBIS.

temperature continues to drop, however, the shivering will decrease, and the victim may actually feel warm. Advanced hypothermia can lead to unconsciousness and even death.

Another hazard of cold weather is frostbite: the freezing of the skin, which causes damage to tissues. There is a risk of exposed skin freezing when the wind chill is below −22°F (−30°C), and it only takes a minute or so for skin to freeze when the wind chill is below −58°F (−50°C). The parts of the body most susceptible to frostbite are the ears, nose, hands, and feet. In the mildest cases of frostbite, while complete recovery is possible, the affected area may feel numb for several months. Serious cases of frostbite can produce a long-term sensitivity to the cold. In the most severe cases, when the tissue freezes to the point that it dies, the affected limb turns black. In such cases the affected area has to be amputated.

The earliest warning sign of impending frostbite is pain in the fingers, toes, or nose. If the pain is followed by numbness, then frostbite is setting in, and it is necessary to get out of the cold immediately. If you can, run the affected area under warm water, from 105°F to 110°F (41°C to 43°C). If the area hurts as it gets warmer, this is a good sign. It means that the tissues are still alive.

Low temperatures are also hard on humans in other ways. Greater stress is placed on the heart as the outer parts of the body become cool. The heart compensates for this by working harder to pump blood to those

Extreme weather: The New England blizzard of 1978

On February 6–7, 1978, southeastern New England suffered its most disruptive snowstorm of the century. The snow was produced by a low-pressure system that remained stationary for more than twenty-four hours just off the eastern tip of Long Island. At the same time, a strong, northeasterly wind known as a nor'easter blew in from southern Canada. The snowstorm, which came just seventeen days after a previous blizzard, claimed at least fifty lives. Most of the deaths were due to overexertion while shoveling snow.

Over a thirty-hour period, heavy snow fell on the upper Chesapeake Bay area, Long Island, parts of eastern Massachusetts, central Rhode Island, eastern Connecticut, Vermont, and New Hampshire. Both Boston and Providence received more than 3 feet (0.9 meter) of snow. Some parts of Rhode Island reported 4 feet (1.2 meters) of snow. The storm also brought significant snowfall to New York City, New Jersey, and eastern Pennsylvania.

The weather paralyzed traffic, caused power outages, and forced businesses to close in Rhode Island, Connecticut, and Massachusetts for the better part of a week. President Jimmy Carter declared emergencies in those three states. In many parts of New England driving in nonemergency cases was banned, and violators were slapped with hefty fines.

Gale-force winds shook much of the region during the storm. A gust measuring 79 miles (127 kilometers) per hour was reported at Boston's Logan Airport, with a two-day wind-speed average at the airport of 30 miles (48 kilometers) per hour. Hurricane-force winds greater than 74 miles (119 kilometers) per hour blasted Massachusetts' eastern shore. Those winds combined with high tides to produce colossal waves that smashed into coastal communities. More damage was caused by coastal flooding during that storm than from any hurricane affecting New England to that date.

More than one thousand army troops from the Midwest and the South were flown to New England to assist in the cleanup from the storm. Over 140 military aircraft, carrying nearly 7 million pounds (3.2 million kilograms) of snow-clearing equipment, landed at airports in Boston, Providence, and Hartford, Connecticut, for use in the effort.

areas. Strenuous activity, such as shoveling snow, can bring on heart attacks—especially in older people or people with histories of heart trouble.

Are humans causing blizzards?

The Blizzard of January 1996, which produced record-breaking snowfalls on the East Coast and caused more than one hundred deaths, made some scientists wonder if global warming was bringing on strong blizzards and other types of extreme weather. Many scientists agree that global average

Vehicles are abandoned along a Massachusetts road in the deep snow left by the blizzard of 1978. AP IMAGES.

temperatures have begun to rise and will continue to rise, because of an increase of certain gases in Earth's atmosphere. According to the U.S. Environmental Protection Agency (EPA), global average temperatures have increased by 1°F (0.5°C) in the last century. Much of this global climate change, especially during the last fifty years, may be due to human activity.

Human activities have caused the build-up of greenhouse gases in Earth's atmosphere. These gases are called greenhouse gases because they let sunlight come in but don't let heat go back out into space—as if Earth were covered with a big glass greenhouse that keeps everything warm. The most plentiful greenhouse gases are water vapor and carbon dioxide. Other greenhouse gases include methane and nitrous oxide.

The increase of carbon dioxide in the atmosphere is believed to be the main reason for global warming. Carbon dioxide is produced by burning fossil fuels, such as coal, fuel oil, gasoline, and natural gas, and is emitted into the air by homes, factories, and motorized vehicles. During the last century, the amount of carbon dioxide in the atmosphere has increased by 30 percent. During that same period, the planet has become, on average, slightly more than 1°F (0.5°C) warmer.

There doesn't seem to be much doubt that humans have affected global warming by burning fossil fuels and other activities, but is that activity making blizzards more frequent and more intense?

A man in Brooklyn, New York, shovels snow after a blizzard in 2006. AP IMAGES.

Some say yes; others no   Some scientists say global warming causes more water to evaporate from the oceans into the atmosphere. When this warmer, moister air collides with colder air, it can produce more ice crystals and stronger winds, which can result in stronger blizzards. They also say that because this evaporation process is going on all the time, it also produces a steady supply of moist air, which can result in more frequent blizzards.

Other scientists point out that global warming should also warm the colder regions and therefore produce less cold air to collide with the warm, moist air. This should produce fewer blizzards, they claim. They also note that in many areas, no real increase in the amount of moisture in the air has occurred. These scientists claim that although global warming is real, it has not resulted in more frequent or more intense blizzards.

Technology connection

There are many ways to predict, prepare for, and respond to blizzards. Today's weather forecasters use satellite images, radar, data from weather stations on the ground, and computer models to determine where and when blizzards are forming.

In blizzard-prone regions, residents attempt to lessen the impact of the storms by erecting snow fences, which reduce drifts on roads. They also maintain fleets of snowplows for snow removal, stock salt for melting

A Chicago expressway after a snowstorm paralyzed the area in 1967.

ice, and stock sand for providing traction on slippery roads. When a blizzard starts, snow-plows and salt and sand spreaders are dispatched to keep roads open—at least for use by emergency vehicles.

Weather satellites   Weather satellites, circling the globe in space, provide meteorologists with pictures and other information about blizzards and other storms. The first weather satellite, called TIROS 1 (Television Infrared Observation Satellite), was launched in April 1960. Today, several nations operate satellites that continuously monitor global weather.

For most people, the words "weather satellite" conjure up images of swirling clouds that are seen on television newscasts. While weather satellites do produce those photos, they also perform other functions. Weather satellites determine the temperature throughout the atmosphere, from the cloud tops down to the land and oceans. They also measure humidity and wind speeds in the upper air and even track plumes of invisible water vapor. Weather satellites give meteorologists their first look at blizzards and other storms forming over land or sea. Once a developing storm is spotted, it is probed in greater detail using Doppler radar located on the ground.

Doppler radar   Doppler radar is a sophisticated type of radar that relies on the Doppler Effect—when a wave, like a radio wave, bounces off a moving object, it changes the frequency of the wave. Scientists use this technique to determine wind speed and direction, as well as the direction in which precipitation is moving. Radar, which is an abbreviation for "radio detection and ranging," works by emitting short radio waves, called microwaves, that reflect off clouds and raindrops. This information allows forecasters to identify potential blizzards in their earliest stages.

In 1996 a network of 156 high-powered Doppler radars, called NEX-RAD (Next Generation Weather Radar), was installed across the United States. Data from these radars around the nation are sent, via high-speed computers, to National Weather Service (NWS) centers and field offices

Extreme weather: The great Midwest blizzard of 1967

One of the largest blizzards on record for the Midwest came on January 26–27, 1967. The storm of snow and ice affected central and northern Illinois, central and northern Indiana, southeast Iowa, lower Michigan, Missouri, and Kansas. Kalamazoo, Michigan, received 28 inches (71 centimeters) of snow. Gary, Indiana, and Chicago, Illinois, both reported 24 inches (61 centimeters).

The blizzard was produced by a storm system that formed over the Gulf of Mexico and traveled north to the Ohio River Valley. The system had brought unseasonably warm weather to the Midwest in the five-day period prior to the blizzard. Then on January 24, just two days before the blizzard, a cold air mass arrived from the North. The combination of warm and cold air produced severe thunderstorms and tornadoes. The tornadoes tore through Missouri, Illinois, and Iowa. They killed several people and damaged or destroyed 200 houses.

On January 26 the weather changed sharply in Chicago. While lightning still flickered in the sky, the temperature dropped and the wind picked up. Snow began falling and a blizzard was soon underway. A record-setting 24 inches (61 centimeters) of snow fell in a little more than twenty-nine hours. Winds clocked at 50 miles (80 kilometers) per hour, and gusting to 60 miles (97 kilometers) per hour, piled up snowdrifts 20 feet (6.6 meters) high. There were seventy-six deaths due to the storm, most of them in Chicago.

Chicago remained at a stand-still for several days under 24 million tons (22 metric tons) of snow. The city was a tangled mass of stranded cars, taxicabs, and trucks. More than three hundred city buses and even some snowplows were among the stalled vehicles. The city's expressways looked like huge parking lots. Long-distance and commuter train service was suspended. Chicago's O'Hare Field (now O'Hare International Airport), one of the busiest airports in the world, was closed for a record three days.

In central Illinois, central Indiana, Missouri, and Kansas the snow, plus sleet and freezing rain, brought down power lines and put much of the region in a blackout. National Guardsmen were called out to help with snow removal in Indiana.

around the country. At the NWS' Storm Prediction Center in Norman, Oklahoma, meteorologists analyze weather data from Doppler radars and other systems twenty-four hours a day. When they detect conditions that could give rise to winter storms, they notify the weather center in that area. The local weather center may then issue a winter storm alert.

Computer-based prediction   Computer-based prediction relies on a sophisticated computer program called a numerical prediction model. The model incorporates mathematical equations that mimic processes in nature. When data from weather instruments is entered into a computer,

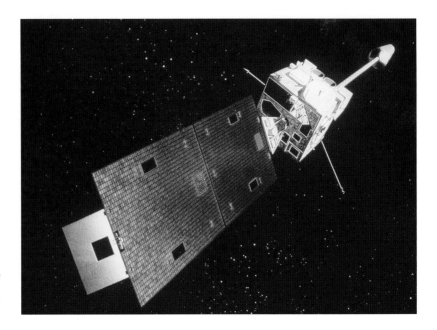

The Geostationary Operational Environmental Satellite (GOES) system. ©CORBIS.

the program projects how the weather will change over the next twelve hours, twenty-four hours, forty-eight hours, and several days into the future.

Due to improved computer forecasting models in recent years, the amount of time between when a blizzard warning is issued and when the storm strikes has greatly increased. In fact, major storms can now be predicted by computer even before their associated conditions are detected by weather stations.

Snow fences   Snow fences are devices that slow winds and reduce the blowing and drifting of snow. They are erected along highways to reduce the amount of snow that ends up on the road. As the wind whips across a clearing, it picks up snow. When the snow-laden wind hits a snow fence, it slows down. The wind then deposits its snow, forming a gradual drift on the other (downwind) side of the snow fence.

A snow fence must be placed far enough from the road to allow room for the snowdrift to form, without reaching the road. The rule of thumb is that snow will accumulate downwind of the fence for a distance approximately ten times the height of the fence. Therefore, if a fence is 10 feet (3 meters) high, it should be placed at least 100 feet (30 meters) from the road.

A snow fence near a highway in Wyoming. ©TED SPIEGEL/CORBIS.

Salting icy roads   Salt is applied to snowy, icy roads because it melts ice and prevents the water from refreezing. Salt is also relatively cheap and easy to apply, making it the de-icing agent of choice since the 1960s.

Sodium chloride (NaCl), the type of salt used on roads, melts ice through an equilibrium change. Ice on the ground is in a state of dynamic equilibrium between the liquid and the solid states. When sodium chloride comes into contact with the ice, it is dissolved. When dissolved, sodium chloride breaks down into one positively charged sodium ion (Na+) and a negatively charged chloride ion (Cl–). At the same time it causes the water molecules making up the ice to disassociate into one hydroxide ion, OH–, and one hydronium ion, H+. The positively charged hydrogen atoms are drawn to the negatively charged chloride atoms, and negatively charged oxygen atoms are drawn to the sodium atoms.

Experiment: Freezing salty water

Normally, water freezes at 32°F (0°C). However, salt can be used to lower the freezing point of water. This is why some communities throw salt on roadways during winter storms. To demonstrate how this works, take two cups of water of the same size. The water should be the same temperature. Place a tablespoon or so of salt in one of the cups and place both cups in the freezer. Then check each cup every ten minutes or so. You'll see that the cup of plain water freezes before the cup of salty water. This is because a chemical reaction between the salt and the water lowers the water's freezing point. You can vary this experiment by doing more trials in which you add more or less salt. The more salt you add, the colder the water will have to become before it freezes.

The sodium and chloride ions bond with the hydronium and hydroxide ions so that hydronium and hydroxide are not free to recombine into water. The sodium and chloride ions also draw water molecules away from one another. Salt, in this way, both prevents liquid water molecules from forming ice crystals and breaks up existing ice crystals. The speed of melting is increased, while the speed of freezing is not changed. Sodium chloride is only effective at melting ice at temperatures down to 20°F (−7°C).

Whereas salt provides an efficient means of melting snow and ice on roads and has greatly contributed to highway safety, it also has a downside. Salt is bad for the environment. It kills vegetation along the side of the road and can seep down into wells, making the water undrinkable. Salt also causes vehicles to rust and bridges to corrode. For these reasons, salt is applied only in the minimum quantities necessary to get the job done.

A matter of survival

The National Weather Service issues blizzard warnings whenever blizzard conditions are expected. If forecasters predict a winter storm that is less severe than a blizzard, but still serious enough to create dangerous travel conditions, they will issue another type of winter storm alert. Four classes of winter storm alerts, based on the seriousness of the storm, are defined as follows:

- **A winter weather advisory** states that snow, sleet, freezing rain, or high winds may be on the way. It advises people to exercise caution when traveling.

- **A winter storm watch** states that at least 6 inches of snow and an ice storm may be on the way. It advises people to limit their travels and to exercise great caution if they must venture onto the roads.

- **A winter storm warning** states that a storm, including heavy snow and possibly ice, has already begun or will soon begin. It advises people not to travel, except in an emergency.

- **A blizzard warning** states that a blizzard—including blowing or falling snow, low temperatures, and winds of at least 35 miles

Reports from the past: Tragedy at Donner Pass

One of the most famous blizzard-related tragedies in history occurred during the winter of 1846–47 in the Sierra Nevada Mountains of California. A group of eighty-seven pioneers, including men, women, and children, left Illinois for California in April 1846. The group, led by George and Jacob Donner, was known as the Donner Party.

On October 31, the Donner Party began their ascent into the mountains in northeastern California. When they reached a pass (today called Donner Pass) at an altitude of 7,085 feet (2,160 meters), the snow and wind forced them to a halt. A few members of the party pressed on to seek help, while the others erected shelters and prepared to wait for better weather.

The snow and wind relentlessly blasted the pioneers in the mountain pass. Some drifts reached 60 feet high. "We cannot see twenty feet looking against the wind," Donner Party member J. F. Reed wrote in his diary, "I dread the coming night."

Before long the group's food supplies ran out. The oxen they had planned to kill and eat had become lost in the snowstorms. For a time the pioneers lived on mice and twigs; then the winter became so severe that people dared not venture outside. Forty people died of disease or starvation in the following months. In time, the survivors became so desperate and addled by starvation that members of the party resorted to eating their own dead. Food supplies were finally brought to the trapped group in February 1847 after the men who had gone for help finally reached the Sacramento Valley and organized a rescue party.

Today a major highway and railroad tracks connecting San Francisco with Reno, Nevada, run through the Donner Pass. The Donner Memorial State Park was erected near the pass to commemorate the pioneers who lived and died through that terrible winter.

Drawing of the Donner Party's winter settlement in Salt Lake, California. ©BETTMANN/CORBIS.

Forest service employees measuring snow depth.

(56 kilometers) per hour—is on the way. The combination of moving snow and low clouds make it appear that the ground and sky are a continuous white sheet (called a whiteout), making travel nearly impossible. It advises people to remain indoors.

Preparing for blizzards   If you live in an area affected by winter storms, it is wise to take the following precautions at the start of the season:

- Store extra blankets and warm clothing and boots for every member of the family.
- Put together a supplies kit for your home containing first aid materials, a battery-powered flashlight, a battery-powered radio, extra batteries, nonperishable food, a nonelectric can opener, and bottled water.
- Store a similar supplies kit in the trunk of your car, plus a shovel, a bag of sand, tire chains, jumper cables, and a piece of brightly colored cloth to tie to your antenna.
- Keep your car's gas tank full to prevent the fuel line from freezing.

Tips for outdoor survival   If you must go outside during a winter storm, follow these rules:

- Be aware of the current temperature and wind chill. When dangerous conditions are present, only venture out for short periods.

- Wear several layers of lightweight clothing, mittens, a warm hat with ear flaps, a scarf covering your face and neck, warm socks, and waterproof boots. Wear wool clothing closest to your skin. (Wool will trap your body heat even if it gets wet.) Wear a brightly colored coat.
- Don't venture out alone.
- Walk carefully over icy ground.
- When shoveling snow, take frequent breaks to avoid overexertion.
- If you must drive, inform someone of your route, destination, and expected time of arrival.
- Stay away from downed wires—they can cause burns or electrocution. Report downed wires to the power company.
- If you're trapped outdoors in a blizzard, dig a large hole in the snow and climb in. This "snow cave," as it is called, will protect you from the wind and decrease the rate at which your body loses heat.

Surviving a blizzard in your car   If you get stranded in your car during a blizzard, follow these rules:

- Stay with your car. Tie the brightly colored cloth to your antenna so rescuers can spot you. Don't attempt to walk away! It's easy to become disoriented and lose your way in a snowstorm.
- Only start the car and turn on the heater for ten minutes out of every hour. When the car is running, leave on the inside light so you can be spotted. When the car is not running, periodically check the tailpipe and clear it of snow, if necessary. If your tailpipe is blocked, dangerous exhaust fumes can back up into the car.
- Move your arms and legs continuously to stay warm and maintain your blood circulation.
- Let in fresh air by slightly opening the window that's opposite the direction of the blowing wind.

[*See Also* **Forecasting; Precipitation; Weather: An Introduction**]

For More Information

BOOKS

Allaby, Michael. *Blizzards.* 2nd ed. New York: Facts on File, 2003.

Cable, Mary. *The Blizzard of '88.* New York: Antheneum, 1988.

Erlbach, Arlene. *Blizzards.* Chicago: Children's Press, 1995.

Hopping, Lorraine Jean. *Blizzards!* New York: Scholastic Inc., 1998.

Rosenfeld, Jeffrey P. *Eye of the Storm: Inside the World's Deadliest Hurricanes, Tornadoes, and Blizzards.* New York: Basic Books, 2005.

WEB SITES

Blizzard of 1996. *National Snow and Ice Data Center.* <http://nsidc.org/snow/blizzard/> (accessed August 17, 2006).

Historical Winter Storms. *The Weather Channel.* <http://www.weather.com/encyclopedia/winter/history.html> (accessed August 17, 2006).

Northeastern Regional Climate Center. <http://www.nrcc.cornell.edu/> (accessed August 17, 2006).

USA Today Weather. *USA Today.* <http://asp.usatoday.com/weather/weatherfront.aspx> (accessed August 17, 2006).

Drought

A drought (pronounced DROWT) is an extended period where the amount of rain or snow that falls on an area is much lower than usual. A drought usually lasts at least one season and sometimes continues for years. It may affect an area the size of several states or greater. During a drought, the amount of water used by plants, animals, and people is much greater than the precipitation, which is the amount of water that falls to the ground in the form of rain or snow. Rivers and lakes may dry up. Droughts happen almost everywhere in the world, although some areas experience drought more frequently than others.

There is no universal definition of drought based on rainfall amounts, since what is considered usual varies from region to region and climate to climate. In Australia, which is a dry climate, a drought is defined as a year in which precipitation is less than 10 percent of average. In the United States—most of which has a temperate, humid climate—drought is defined as a period at least twenty-one days long during which rainfall over an extensive area is less than 30 percent of average. In places with distinct wet and dry seasons, such as India, a drought is defined as a year in which precipitation is less than 75 percent of average. The severity of a drought is determined by the amount of rainfall, the water levels in rivers and lakes, the duration of the dry spell, and the size of the area affected.

Droughts lead to crop losses, soil erosion, death of livestock, and even famine (long-term shortages of food that can lead to hunger, malnutrition, and death). Human beings sometimes make drought conditions worse by stripping the land of vegetation and placing heavy demands on the water supply.

The African Sahel: Devastated by drought

The longest-lasting and most devastating drought in recent times occurred in the Sahel region of Africa in the last half of the twentieth

WORDS TO KNOW

air mass: a large quantity of air throughout which temperature and moisture content is fairly constant.

air pressure: the pressure exerted by the weight of air over a given area of Earth's surface. Also called atmospheric pressure or barometric pressure.

aquifer: an underground layer of spongy rock, gravel, or sand in which water collects.

arid: describes a climate in which almost no rain or snow falls.

blocking system: a whirling air mass containing either a high-pressure system (a blocking high) or a low-pressure system (a blocking low), that gets cut off from the main flow of upper-air westerlies.

climate: the weather experienced by a given location, averaged over several decades.

desert climate: the world's driest climate type, with less than 10 inches of rainfall annually.

desertification: the process by which semiarid lands turn into desert (also called land degradation). It is caused by prolonged drought, during which time the top layers of soil dry out and blow away.

drought: an extended period where the amount of rain or snow that falls on an area is much lower than usual.

ecosystem: a community of plants and animals, including humans, and their physical surroundings.

El Niño: means "the Christ child" in Spanish. A period of unusual warming of the Pacific Ocean waters off the coast of Peru and Ecuador. It usually starts around Christmas, which is how it got its name.

erosion: the wearing away of a surface by the action of wind, water, or ice.

global water budget: the balance of the volume of water coming and going between the oceans, atmosphere, and continental landmasses.

heat cramps: muscle cramps or spasms, usually afflicting the abdomen or legs, that may occur during exercise in hot weather.

Heat exhaustion: a form of mild shock that results when fluid and salt are lost through heavy perspiration.

heat stroke: a life-threatening condition that sets in when heat exhaustion is left untreated and the body has exhausted its efforts to cool itself. Also called sunstroke.

heat wave: an extended period of high heat and humidity.

La Niña: Spanish for "little girl," a period of unusual cooling of the Pacific Ocean waters off the coast of Peru and Ecuador. It often follows an El Niño.

semiarid: a climate in which very little rain or snow falls.

transpiration: the process by which plants emit water through tiny pores in the underside of their leaves.

upper-air westerlies: global-scale, upper-air winds that flow in waves heading west to east (but also shifting north and south) through the middle latitudes of the Northern Hemisphere.

---

century. The Sahel (Arabic for "margin" or "shore") is a strip of semiarid land in northern Africa, sandwiched between the Sahara to the north and the wetter grasslands to the south. It extends from the continent's west

A man walks on drought-cracked soil in the African country of Mali. ©KAREN KASMAUSKI/CORBIS.

coast almost to its east coast. The Sahel ranges in width from 200 to 700 miles (320 to 1130 kilometers) and covers more than 2.5 million square miles (5.1 million square kilometers). It runs through the countries of Senegal, Mauritania, Mali, Burkina Faso, Niger, Nigeria, Chad, and Sudan. A similar semiarid belt exists in Ethiopia and Somalia. The Sahel region constitutes about 20 percent of the landmass of Africa, and the nations within this region are among the poorest in the world.

The ecosystem of the Sahel is the most fragile in all of Africa. The primary vegetation includes low-growing grass, thorny shrubs, and a few varieties of trees.

During the last thirty years of the twentieth century, the Sahel suffered from desertification—the process of turning the land into desert. In the beginning of desertification, the soil slowly loses its ability to grow plants. Next comes a period of rapid soil breakdown. In the final stage of desertification, the soil becomes unable to hold nutrients or retain enough water to support plant life. Desertification is a long process and is difficult to reverse.

The major cause of desertification in the Sahel has been a series of droughts that lasted for years. Human activity, such as intensive farming and grazing large numbers of livestock, has also contributed to desertification.

Drought is common   Throughout history the Sahel has experienced frequent droughts. The region receives an average of just 4 to 20 inches

(10 to 50 centimeters) of rain per year, mostly in the southern areas during the months of June, July, and August. Because the area is also hot during this period, about 90 percent of the water that falls to the ground returns to the atmosphere through evaporation and transpiration. With the water balance so unsteady in normal times, even a small decrease in rainfall over a season may result in water shortages and crop failures.

After a relatively rainy period in the 1950s and early-to-mid 1960s, a drought started in 1968 and lasted until 1973. During that period, crops died throughout the region, and a famine took the lives of some 250,000 people and 3.5 million grazing animals. Many more people would have died if not for a massive amount of help from other countries.

After a few years of normal rainfall, relatively dry conditions prevailed from 1976 through 1981. Then drought struck the region again from 1983 through 1985 and in the early 1990s. Throughout the dry years, desertification continued its march southward from the Sahara. Overall, between the years 1935 and 1985, a portion of the Sahel, roughly equal in size to the combined size of France and Austria, turned into desert.

By the end of the 1990s, however, normal precipitation levels had returned to the Sahel. While desertification was continuing in some places, much of the Sahel had recovered to the point that local food production needs were being met.

The influence of the people   Although the problem of desertification in the Sahel started because of the long periods of drought, population growth and bad use of the land intensified the problem. Because of the lack of rainfall and high temperatures in the region, the soil is thin, sandy, and fragile. Most of the land is covered with grass and is best used by people who move from one area to another with small herds of animals, or by small-scale farmers.

In years past, Sahel-dwellers grew crops only on a particular piece of land one season at a time. They would then leave that piece of land undisturbed for several years so that the soil could regain its nutrients. During that time, cattle would graze on the crop stubble and fertilize the soil with their wastes.

In the latter half of the 1900s, however, the population of the Sahel increased greatly. Increasingly more land was used for growing crops, which thinned the soil and reduced its fertility. As a result, farmers could not let part of the land sit undisturbed for several years; instead, they had to plant every available piece of land every year in order to produce enough food to survive.

A series of unusually rainy years in the 1950s and 1960s also encouraged more farming in the Sahel. Shortsighted government officials, not anticipating that a drought might return, urged farmers to cultivate greater areas of land. Land previously undisturbed or used for grazing was cleared. The trees and brush were taken for firewood, and the soil was plowed for crops.

Changes in methods of grazing livestock also contributed to desertification. The traditional practice of moving livestock from one area to another to eat the grass changed as small towns were built up around water wells. Thus, the livestock would eat grass only in one area and the land in the surrounding area was stripped bare of grass and other plants. As a result, it became hard and barren within just a few years.

Dry lands that have been stripped of vegetation take a long time to recover. Even when rains do fall, very little water penetrates the earth. Most of the rain runs off the ground, washing away the topsoil and leaving a wasteland. Moreover, the wind causes more erosion when there are no plants and their roots to hold the soil in place.

Millions of people forced to move   During the periods of drought from the late 1960s through the mid 1980s, more than ten million farmers and shepherds from the Sahel moved to cities and towns. They built shanties on the outskirts of already overpopulated urban areas and tried to earn a living. For example, in Mauritania, one of the countries hit hardest by the drought, refugees increased the population of the town of Nuakchott from 20,000 in 1960 to 350,000 in 1987.

The migration of people from country to city has done more than create population pressures on cities; it has disrupted centuries-old ways of life and tribal bonds. Omar Mahmoud, a former herdsman who moved to an urban shantytown in the early 1970s, was trying to live by raising vegetables on a small, dusty plot of land. He told a *National Geographic* reporter, "I don't know much about this work. My life is being with my animals, but now they are all gone. Forty head of cattle, forty sheep. Sixty goats."

Foreign aid has mixed results   Foreign governments and international relief agencies began providing emergency aid to the Sahel in the late 1960s. While this assistance prevented mass starvation in many areas, and a few projects helped slow the pace of desertification, many of the projects were costly and poorly managed; they also did not have much effect on the problems.

Many relief-agency projects involved the planting of trees or grasses in an effort to stabilize the soil and prevent further erosion. In some cases planners planted too few trees, which did not provide enough stability for the soil. In other cases, the planting of trees was not coupled with instructions about the importance of the trees to the people's survival. As a result, many people cut down the trees for firewood. Some agencies made the mistake of providing seeds for crops such as eggplant that were unfamiliar and distasteful to the people living in the region.

In one notable success story, however, the relief agency CARE began a project in the Majja Valley in Niger. They planted a double row of trees along a 230-mile-long (370-kilometer-long) stretch of land. The trees, which have been maintained by local villagers, stop the wind from eroding the soil during dry times and protect crops from the wind during the rainy season.

What can be done in the Sahel?   Scientists have different opinions about what can be done to save the Sahel from drought in the future. Some feel the people must be moved out of the area and the farmlands replaced with forests to prevent future problems. Others feel the people themselves can solve the problems without being moved by exchanging ideas, building water supplies, and planting trees. Everyone seems to agree that a big part of the solution is to develop a society in the Sahel where there are fewer people dependent on the land for their survival and more people doing other jobs.

Recent events: Major droughts since 2000

Between 1999 and 2002, the United States experienced a drought that was among the worst of the past 40 years. During these years of drought, parts of the United States experienced the driest conditions in more than 100 years of record keeping. The year 2001 was the second-hottest on record in the United States, second only to 1998, which saw record temperatures due to El Niño (an extraordinarily strong episode of the annual warming of the Pacific waters off the coast of Peru and Equador).

The consequences of the 1999 to 2002 drought were significant and far reaching. Heat and water restrictions hampered U.S. crop production. Rivers lost water, and fish died by the thousands. People, especially elderly people living in cities, died in their homes from the heat. Wildfires raged and caused millions of dollars worth of damage.

Drought is defined as an extended period of unusually dry conditions. However, drought conditions can and do exist even in years not officially termed "drought" years. In August 2006, for example, the National Weather Service published drought statements for thirty American cities from Talahassee, Florida, to Denver, Colorado, to Duluth, Minnesota.

Even in the absence of an official drought, hot and dry conditions create the risk of wildfires, crop destruction and river evaporation. Many cities throughout the United States experience water shortages during the summer months. City governments sometimes respond by imposing bans on water use for irrigation purposes in order to conserve precious water supplies.

What causes a drought?

Droughts occur when rain-producing clouds fail to form, and there is little, if any, rainfall. Several factors can bring on those conditions. In

Food delivery to Niger, Africa, during the Sahel drought, 1973. ©FARRELL GREHAN/ CORBIS.

Drought conditions in Sebago Lake, Maine, in 2002.
AP MAGES.

temperate regions, including much of the United States, the primary cause of drought is the prolonged presence of a high-pressure system called a blocking high. In many parts of the world, the weather condition known as El Niño (and its sister, La Niña), which occurs about every five to seven years, also influences rainfall amounts. The removal of vegetation can also contribute to drought in some regions.

Blocking highs   The main cause of drought in the United States is the prolonged presence of a high-pressure system over a given area. High-pressure systems generally produce clear skies and little rain. As air descends beneath a high-pressure system, the moisture within it evaporates. Low-pressure systems, in contrast, are associated with cloudiness. The air beneath them rises, and the moisture within the air condenses and forms clouds.

Systems of high and low pressure typically alternate over a given location as they are pushed along by upper-air winds. Those winds circle the globe along a wavy, west-to-east path. Sometimes, however, an air mass (a large quantity of air throughout which pressure, temperature, and moisture content is fairly constant) gets cut off from the main flow of upper-air winds. If that air mass has high pressure, it is called a blocking high; if it has low pressure, it is called a blocking low. The presence of a blocking system typically brings about an extended period of one type of weather.

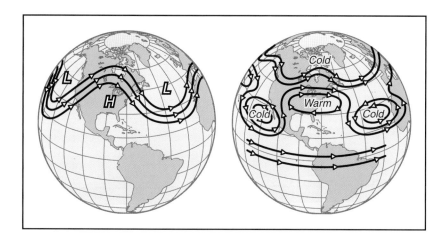

The formation of blocking high (H) and blocking low (L) systems.

A blocking high may remain stationary for several weeks. In addition to producing dry conditions, the blocking high may produce exceedingly hot weather. The surface air heats up because the upper-air circulation, which moderates temperatures by alternating warm and cold air masses, passes around the area.

El Niño and La Niña   In some parts of the world, drought is driven by El Niño (pronounced el NEE-nyo). El Niño is a current of warm water in the tropical Pacific Ocean. Every few years, the water that flows from the western Pacific and settles off the coast of Peru and Ecuador is unusually warm and remains for an extended period of time.

Air pressure across the Pacific Ocean is linked to El Niño. In normal conditions, air pressure is higher over the eastern Pacific, near South America, and lower over the western Pacific, near Australia. (High pressure is typically associated with clear skies, while low pressure is typically associated with cloudy skies and rain.) The difference in pressure between the two areas makes the winds blow from east to west, and toward the equator. The winds carry warmth, moisture, and rainmaking clouds toward Australia and Indonesia.

During an El Niño year, the air pressure in the western Pacific rises while the air pressure in the eastern Pacific lowers. As the warm water in the eastern Pacific evaporates into the air and forms clouds, the normally dry coastal South American nations get more-than-average rainfall, causing flooding and erosion. At the same time, Australia, Indonesia, the

Question: Is global warming causing droughts?

As Earth's climate changes, drought becomes a more regular part of human existence. Many U.S. states now experience drought conditions regularly, and the U.S. experienced its worst drought in almost half a century between 1999 and 2002. Scientists believe that global temperatures are on the rise, but could this be contributing to the increase in drought conditions?

Recent scientific data indicates that the global average temperature increased by about 1°F in the last century. Scientists refer to this process as global warming, which is partly caused by increase of certain gases, called greenhouse gases, in Earth's atmosphere. Many scientists think that temperatures will rise even more in the decades to come, and some are worried that increased temperature will cause more frequent, severe, and prolonged droughts.

Farmer surveying the parched soil on his Texas farm. ©JIM SUGAR/CORBIS.

There are many factors that cause drought, and droughts have plagued humanity for centuries. Certainly global warming is not the only factor that contributes to drought. However, warmer temperatures increase the evaporation of water from Earth's surface, which contributes to and worsens drought conditions.

Philippines, and other lands of the western Pacific experience less-than-average rainfall and sometimes drought.

Often in the wake of El Niño comes La Niña—a period of unusual cooling of the ocean water off the coast of Peru and Ecuador. La Niña's effects on rainfall patterns are practically the opposite of El Niño's. One consequence of La Niña is that drier than usual conditions prevail in many parts of the United States. La Niña also means drought for the South American coast and flooding for the western Pacific region.

The water cycle

The water cycle (also called the hydrologic cycle) is the continuous movement of water between the atmosphere and the Earth's surface (oceans and landmasses). On one side of the equation is precipitation—rain and snow—and on the other side is evaporation—the process by which liquid water at the surface converts to a gas and enters the atmosphere.

From 85 to 90 percent of the moisture that evaporates into the atmosphere comes from the oceans. The rest evaporates from the soil, lakes, and rivers that make up the continental land-masses. Even plants emit water through tiny pores in the underside of their leaves in a process called transpiration.

Some of the moist air above oceans is carried over land by the wind. Clouds form and drop rain and snow on the ground. When precipitation hits the ground, it either sinks in or runs off, depending on the surface composition. On soft ground, most of the water sinks into the soil to be absorbed by plant roots or to seep down into underground aquifers. Some of it runs off into streams and

rivers. If the water strikes a hard surface, like rock or pavement, most of it runs directly into streams or artificial drains. Eventually this water also flows into rivers.

The oceans lose water in this portion of the cycle—more water evaporates from them than returns as precipitation. The oceans get this water back when the rivers empty their water back into the oceans. Thus the global water budget—the volume of water coming and going from the oceans, atmosphere, and continental land-masses—is kept in balance.

If the water cycle is kept in balance, that means that global precipitation levels remain fairly con-stant. So why do droughts occur? The answer is that rain and snow do not consistently fall in equal amounts in any given place. Moisture may evaporate from one place, travel through the atmosphere, and fall to the ground as rain in another. It is possible, then, for a given location to get lots of rainfall one year and almost no rainfall the next.

Aftermath: The effects of drought

While drought does not produce the sensational pictures of destruction seen in other natural disasters, its economic impact is often greater and longer lasting. According to the Nebraska-based National Drought Mit-igation Center, the average yearly economic damage done by droughts in the United States is greater than the economic damage done by floods and hurricanes combined. Droughts cost the United States between $6 billion and $8 billion per year, while the annual cost of floods and hurricanes are $2.4 billion and $1.2 billion, respectively.

The impact of droughts varies widely, depending on the severity and length of the drought and its location. Among the consequences of drought

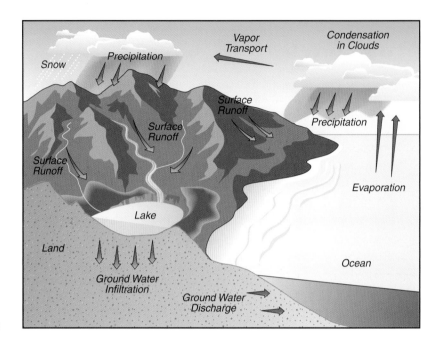

The water cycle.

are shortages of water, livestock and wildlife death, crop loss, soil erosion, wildfires, and dust storms. Famine is the most drastic consequence of drought and is most likely to occur in poor nations where food supplies are already scarce and governments have little money for importing food or drilling wells.

Reduction in water levels   One direct consequence of drought is a shortage of water. Wells run dry, and water levels drop in lakes and rivers. The first water supply to be affected is aquifers, which are underground water reservoirs made of porous rock, gravel, or sand. Aquifers feed lakes and rivers; the top of an aquifer is higher than the bed of the lake or river it feeds. When water is plentiful and an aquifer is full, water runs over into a surface body of water. During drought, however, the level of the aquifer falls below the floor of the lake or river, and the aquifer ceases to replenish the surface body of water. In severe drought, aquifers go dry, and lake and river levels become very low. Wells (holes drilled into aquifers that provide people with water) also may run dry, in which case it becomes necessary to continue drilling to tap sources of water deeper underground.

Experiment: How rainfall affects soil

During a drought, rainfall is extremely scarce. To understand some of rain's effects, try this experiment. Get two large disposable aluminum baking pans. Fill one with some dirt from a garden or yard. Use a pair of scissors or an awl to poke six or eight small holes in one end of the pan that is full of dirt. Put the empty pan under the side of the dirt-filled pan that has holes in it. Lift up the opposite end of the pan (you can use books to hold it up), and then use a watering can to pour water onto the dirt at the elevated end of the pan. Notice what happens to the dirt when the water comes into contact with it, and pay attention to the color of the water as it runs into the second pan.

The lowering of water levels in lakes and rivers has several consequences. For one, fish and other forms of aquatic life may die. If bodies of water become too shallow for boats to operate, the water recreation industry suffers economic harm. If barges and ships cannot carry goods down waterways, the increased cost of shipping materials over land gets passed on to consumers. In addition, the amount of electricity produced by hydroelectric power stations (facilities at which the energy of the moving water is converted into electricity) decreases when rivers flow less forcefully.

The reduction in water levels that results from a drought are felt long after the rains resume. First, enough rain has to fall to recharge dried-out aquifers. This process typically takes a year or more. Only when the aquifers are full will the water begin its slow journey to rivers and lakes.

Migration and famine   When drought is serious enough to affect food and water supplies, people in the affected region are forced to move to another area or subsist on donated food. In Africa, Asia, and Australia—regions where there have been droughts lasting several years—the loss of crops and cattle has caused widespread human suffering. A severe drought in northern China in 1876, for instance, caused crop failures that led to the deaths of millions of people. As many as five million people died in Russia as a result of a drought along the Volga River basin in 1921.

Secondary impacts   Droughts also have indirect impacts, such as increased prices for food, energy, lumber, and other products; unemployment (in the agricultural, forestry, and fishing industries); and the closing of businesses in the affected area. The loss of crops that results from drought does not just

affect the pocketbooks of farmers. It also means a reduction in revenues for merchants who provide goods and services to farmers.

The human factor

While drought on Earth is older than human existence, human activity in recent years has contributed to the frequency and severity of droughts. The primary way in which people bring about drought is by stripping the land of vegetation. Denuded land not only suffers more than covered land during times of drought, but the lack of vegetation also contributes to the occurrence of drought. The major ways in which people encourage drought are through farming intensively, overgrazing cattle, and cutting down trees for timber or fuel.

The concept of surviving a drought has different meanings depending on the location and severity of the drought. For some people, especially those in poor nations, surviving a drought means subsisting on donated food or migrating to wetter regions. In wealthier nations, where food is more abundant, people learn to change their behaviors to adapt to chronic drought rather than aiming merely to survive it. Coping with drought may entail conserving water and keeping cool in hot weather.

Desertification   Desertification, also called land degradation, is the process of turning an area into desert. Approximately 25,000 square miles

A family struggles through a drought in Ethiopia's Tigre region in 2000. ©JOUANNEAU THOMAS/CORBIS SYGMA.

(64,750 square kilometers) of Earth's surface is turned into desert each year. Reversing desertification is a lengthy and difficult process.

While drought is the primary cause of desertification, humans can make the problem worse by removing a land's natural vegetation. Exposed soil is susceptible to erosion by wind and rain. In the absence of roots to bind the soil together and trees and shrubs to slow the wind, heavy rains create deep ravines and gullies in the land, and the wind blows away the topsoil.

The enforcement of travel restrictions across political boundaries in Africa and Asia in the twentieth century has been one of the leading causes of human-induced land degradation in those areas. Prior to the restriction of travel across national borders, nomads roamed with their herds in search of vegetation. New policies forced herdsmen to settle in particular areas, and wells were drilled to meet their water needs. As a result, the settled areas have been overgrazed and stripped of vegetation, and the water levels of the reservoirs feeding those wells have greatly decreased.

Vegetation loss and the cycle of drought   The clearing of vegetation also acts as a deterrent against cloud formation and rain—in essence creating a cycle of drought. When water evaporates from leaves, that water condenses to form clouds, which can cause precipitation. In the absence of plants, the air is dry and does not form clouds. When it does rain, the lack of vegetation also means the surface is less able to retain the water. The water runs off and erodes the soil, which means even fewer plants can grow—making the cycle repeat and grow worse.

Overuse of groundwater   Another practice that creates many problems during droughts is the overuse of groundwater. Groundwater is water from rain or melted snow that seeps into underground aquifers. Pumps are used to tap groundwater for community needs. If the rate of groundwater usage is not reduced during dry periods, aquifers can become depleted, thus contributing to the lowering of lake and river levels.

When aquifers become depleted they may collapse, causing the ground around them to sink—thus forming sinkholes. A sinkhole is a large depression in the Earth's surface; often shaped like a funnel, it is typically 50 feet (15.3 meters) in diameter and up to 100 feet (30.5 meters) deep.

Conserving water   In the United States, water conservation measures are typically required in times of drought; nonessential uses of water, such as car-washing and lawn-watering, are banned. Some communities have programs in place to recycle wastewater (from sources such as bathtubs and dishwashers) for use on small farms and domestic gardens.

There are many ways people can reduce water consumption. For example, people can take showers instead of baths. A bath typically uses 30 gallons (114 liters) of water, whereas a five-minute shower, at a flow of 5 gallons (19 liters) per minute, uses 25 gallons (95 liters) of water. An economy showerhead reduces the flow to 2.5 gallons (9.5 liters) per minute and would use only 12.5 gallons (47.5 liters) for a five-minute shower. If each person in a family of four takes a bath every day for a week, the family uses 840 gallons (3,180 liters) of water. If the family installs an economy showerhead, and each person takes a five-minute shower each day instead of a bath, however, they will use just 280 gallons (1,060 liters) of water. This would save 560 gallons (2,120 liters) of water a week.

Another water-saving device is a low-flow toilet. This type of toilet uses less than 2 gallons (7.6 liters) per flush, as compared to the 5 gallons (19 liters) per flush used by a conventional toilet. Some states in drier regions of the United States have laws requiring the installation of reduced-flow showerheads and toilets in new construction.

Some people conserve water by collecting rainwater and using it for watering the garden. When rainfall is minimal, bath water can be used on the garden. Another method of saving water is installing plumbing that routes

Drought in Australia

Australia experienced a serious drought in the early twenty-first century. The drought, the worst in two decades, began in March 2002. Like the U.S. drought of the same year, the Australian drought produced record-breaking low amounts of rainfall.

The consequences of the Australian drought have been dire. Livestock and crops were particularly hard hit. Because the country had less to export, its trade deficit soared to its highest point in years. Bush fires caused damage and destruction throughout the country.

Animal skeletons during a drought in New South Wales, Australia, in 1982. ©PENNY TWEEDIE/CORBIS.

bath water or water that has been used for washing dishes to the toilet, for flushing.

Community water-saving initiatives have been shown to work. In Tucson, Arizona, where conservation is mandated, residents use an average of 160 gallons (606 liters) of water per day. In Phoenix, by comparison, where water-conservation measures are not required, residents use an average of 260 gallons (984 liters) per day.

The heat factor   Heat waves (extended periods of high heat), which are frequently associated with drought and actually worsen the effects of drought, are among the leading causes of death during droughts. Under drought conditions there are few, if any, clouds to block the incoming solar energy. The sunlight heats the land and robs it of existing moisture by causing rapid evaporation. The loss of moisture, in turn, makes the air even hotter. When the

How to survive a heat wave

The following suggestions can help you stay healthy during hot weather:

- Avoid overexertion, especially during the hottest part of the day. The coolest part of day, and the safest time for strenuous activity, is between 4 AM and 7 AM.

- Wear loose, lightweight, light-colored clothing. This type of clothing allows air to circulate while protecting the skin from the Sun's heat and damaging rays. The light color reflects, rather than absorbs, sunlight.

- Remain indoors as much as possible. If you don't have air conditioning, stay on the first floor, out of the sunshine, and keep the air circulating with electric fans. Each day that the air is very hot, try to spend some time in an air-conditioned environment.

- Drink plenty of fluids, even if you don't feel thirsty. Water is best. Avoid drinks with caffeine or alcohol, since they actually draw fluids out of the body, which may lead to dehydration.

- Eat frequent, small meals. Avoid foods high in protein since the digestion of protein increases your body's temperature.

- Avoid overexposure to the Sun. When skin is sunburned, its ability to dissipate heat is hampered.

- If you are taking medication that affects your blood circulation, ask your doctor how that medication affects your ability to tolerate heat.

- Groups of people most susceptible to heat-related illness include elderly people, small children, people with chronic illnesses, overweight people, and people with alcohol dependency. People in those groups should be especially cautious during a heat wave.

ground is dry, all incoming solar energy heats the land (as opposed to being absorbed in the process of evaporation) and is transferred directly into the air.

Hot weather adversely affects human health by raising the body's temperature. High body temperature can lead to dehydration, heat exhaustion (a form of mild shock that results when fluids and salt are lost through heavy perspiration), and heat stroke (a life-threatening condition that sets in when heat exhaustion is left untreated, and the body has used up its efforts to cool itself). People engaged in physical activity in hot conditions, particularly if they don't drink enough water, may fall victim to one or more heat-related illnesses.

Heat also places added stresses on the body's circulatory system. For elderly people or people with serious illnesses, that added stress can prove fatal. The most common causes of death in hot weather are cardiac arrest, stroke, and respiratory distress.

Heat waves take more lives than any other type of weather calamity. They kill approximately one thousand people per year, on average, in the United States, and a far greater number in other less-developed countries. In contrast, winter storms or cold kill approximately 130 to 200 people per year, on average, in the United States; floods kill 100 to 160; tornadoes kill 80 to 130; and hurricanes kill 40 to 60 people.

The technology connection

Several technological innovations are used to monitor and respond to droughts. Earth survey satellites provide data about water levels in surface bodies of water and the moisture content of the soil. Irrigation systems, dams, drought-resistant crops, and soil management techniques are all used to make the effects of drought less severe.

Satellite view of the Tambopata River in southeast Peru. © KEVIN SCHAFER/ CORBIS.

Drought prediction, however, remains something of a mystery. Droughts are hard to foresee because they are produced by the *absence* of events in the atmosphere; notably, the absence of rain clouds and precipitation. Other weather phenomena, such as hurricanes, thunderstorms, and blizzards, all have recognizable patterns of clouds and precipitation and show up on weather sensing instruments.

At the end of the twentieth century, researchers were looking at data on the cycles of El Niño and La Niña, as well as trends shown in satellite images, for possible keys to predicting future droughts.

Earth survey satellites   Starting with the launch of Landsat 1 in 1972, a series of Landsat Earth survey satellites have continually monitored drought conditions by providing information on moisture levels in the soil, as well as the depths of lakes and rivers. Two Landsats continue to transmit information: Landsat 5, launched in 1984, and Landsat 7, launched in April 1999. The satellites orbit Earth about fifteen times every day at an altitude of 438 miles (705 kilometers). Each satellite is capable of observing almost every continental surface on the globe in an eighteen-day period. It can determine moisture content in areas as small as ten football fields.

Moisture content in the soil and evaporation rates (both measured by satellites) are reliable indicators of drought. Researchers combine this information with data on precipitation, temperature, and other factors to predict the length and intensity of a drought.

The images returned by Landsat satellites are also used for monitoring deforestation, receding glaciers, and crop growth. They are used to locate mineral deposits and to observe patterns of strip mining, logging, and damage due to insect infestations and fire.

Agricultural practices   One way that farmers protect the soil from the impact of drought is by planting rows of trees or shrubs, called windbreaks, at intervals throughout their fields. Windbreaks, which run crossways to the direction that the wind usually blows, slow the wind and keep it from blowing away the soil.

In some regions with low levels of rainfall, farmers find success through fallow farming, which is the practice of letting one-half of the land lie fallow, or idle, every other year, while planting the other half. During the growing season, the farmer plows the fallow land to unearth weeds. Plowing also creates spaces in the soil that can trap water and raise the moisture content of the soil. When the previously fallow land is planted the following year, seeds are more likely to germinate rapidly, and crops will have an early growth spurt.

Another way that farmers guard against the effects of drought is by planting drought-resistant crops (plants that thrive even in dry conditions). These crops are relatively small and quick to grow. One crop that is drought-resistant is sorghum (pronounced SOAR-gum). During dry periods, sorghum stops growing and reduces transpiration (the loss of water through its leaves); it resumes growing when rain comes. Another example of a crop that does well in dry conditions is alfalfa, the roots of which extend down 6 feet (1.8 meters) or more and tap into groundwater.

Irrigation   Irrigation is the transportation of water from reservoirs or wells to areas where crops are growing. Since the beginning of civilization, farmers have practiced irrigation as a means of improving their ability to grow crops. Irrigated farmland, in general, is twice as productive as nonirrigated farmland. In 2000, more than 900 million square miles

Soil and water in rows.

(6 billion square kilometers) of farmland around the world were irrigated. About one-third of the world's food supply comes from irrigated land.

Irrigation, however, has its drawbacks. For one thing, it is expensive; the drilling of wells and purchase of irrigation equipment and fuel, and in some cases the water, is costly. Many farmers relying on irrigation have found themselves buried in debt. Irrigation is also wasteful. In hot, dry weather, up to one-third of water sprayed out of crop sprinklers evaporates before reaching the ground. Irrigation that relies on groundwater also presents the danger of depleting aquifers. This is particularly hazardous in coastal land, because if the water table falls below sea level, seawater will seep into the aquifer and cause the groundwater to become salty, which destroys the soil.

Dams   The construction of river dams is a common method of storing water and lessening the impact of drought (as well as preventing flooding). A dam is a barrier that blocks a river and controls the flow of water. When a river is dammed, the water backs up in the area behind the dam, creating an artificial lake or reservoir (pronounced REH-zer-vwar). Pipes carry the water from the reservoir to factories, homes, and farms. This ready supply of water is especially useful during times of drought. As the 1990s came to a close, there were more than 60,000 dams in use worldwide.

Large dams—defined as those that are more than 492 feet (150 meters) high, or holding back more than 19.6 million cubic yards (15 million cubic meters) of water—have a significant impact on the surrounding community and environment. When a dam is constructed in a valley, it floods the area upstream, putting homes, farmland, and even whole villages underwater. In the process, it displaces the people who inhabit the area. Dams also disrupt a river's natural cycle of flooding. When a river floods a valley, it deposits a layer of silt that enriches the soil. After the river is dammed, the fertile soil is lost. (The soil upstream is buried beneath the reservoir, and the soil downstream remains exposed but becomes less fertile over time.) Dams also disrupt the balance of the river ecosystem, destroying the habitat of birds, fish, and other animals, as well as many species of plants.

[*See Also* **Climate; Human Influences on Weather and Climate**]

For More Information

BOOKS

Allaby, Michael. *Droughts.* 2nd ed. New York: Facts on File, 2003.

Burby, Liza N. *Heat Waves and Droughts.* New York: Rosen Publishing Group, 1999.

Collier, Michael, and Robert H. Webb. *Floods, Droughts, and Climate Change.* Tucson: University of Arizona Press, 2002.

Stewart, Gail B. *Drought.* New York: Crestwood House, 1990.

Walker, Jane. *Famine, Drought and Plagues.* New York: Gloucester Press, 1992.

Ward, Diane Raines. *Drought, Flood, Folly and the Politics of Thirst.* 1st ed. New York: Riverhead, 2002.

WEB SITES

Drought. *National Weather Service: Hydrologic Information Center.* <http://www.nws.noaa.gov/oh/hic/current/drought/> (accessed August 17, 2006).

Drought Watch. *U.S. Geological Service.* <http://water.usgs.gov/waterwatch/?m=dryw> (accessed August 17, 2006).

NOAA's Drought Information Center. <http://www.drought.noaa.gov/> (accessed August 17, 2006).

U.S. Drought Monitor. *University of Nebraska, Lincoln.* <http://www.drought.unl.edu/dm/monitor.html> (accessed August 17, 2006).

Dust Storm

A dust storm is a large cloud of dust blown by a strong wind. The dust is primarily composed of tiny mineral particles that are lifted high into the atmosphere. The cloud of dust is so dense that it obscures the Sun and may reduce visibility to zero over an area as large as hundreds of thousands of square miles.

Dust storms primarily affect arid (desert) or semiarid (semi-dry) lands where the ground is made of loose soil and sand. They tend not to occur in the driest areas, since the ground is generally hard and flat, with rocks and gravel. Semiarid grassland that has been stripped of vegetation through plowing or overgrazing is particularly susceptible to erosion. Dust storms occur in semiarid land during times of drought, when there is no moisture to bind the soil together.

The areas of the world most prone to dust storms are northern Africa, the Middle East, and central Asia. In many places throughout these regions, dust storms take place from thirty to sixty days per year. Dust storms also occur, although with less frequency, in the arid and semiarid regions of the United States—especially in western Texas and the deserts of southern California, as well as the Great Plains states in the center of the country.

Dust storms can carry material for thousands of miles. Dust from the Sahara Desert settles as far away as Florida and other parts of the U.S. East Coast. Dust storms originating in central Asia have been spotted over the northwest Pacific Ocean, even reaching the West Coast of the United States. In the 1930s, dust from Kansas was deposited throughout the Midwest and the East Coast, and even in the Atlantic Ocean. Texas dust has been identified, through chemical analysis, in every eastern state as well as in portions of Europe.

Dust storms differ from sand storms in that sand storms are composed of sand particles, which are significantly larger than dust particles. Sand storms last a shorter time than dust storms, in general, because the

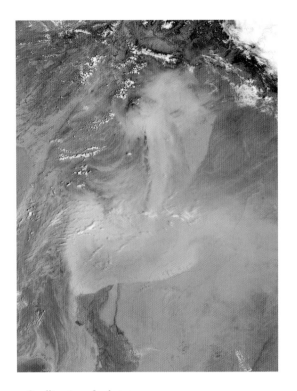

Satellite view of a dust storm swirling south across the Indus Valley in Pakistan, 2006.
©NASA/CORBIS.

heavier sand particles quickly settle to the ground when the wind weakens.

The Dust Bowl

The Dust Bowl is the popular name for the approximately 150,000 square-mile-area (400,000-square-kilometer-area) in the southern portion of the Great Plains region of the United States. This region includes the northern parts of Oklahoma and Texas, southeastern Colorado, western Kansas, and northeastern New Mexico. It is characterized by low annual rainfall, a shallow layer of topsoil, and high winds. The Dust Bowl became well known during the 1930s, when a prolonged drought resulted in violent dust storms.

Pioneers who settled in the Dust Bowl in the 1910s through the 1930s made the mistake of plowing large areas of grassland and planting wheat. As it turned out, the thin, fragile layer of topsoil in the region had been anchored only by the grasses' intricate system of roots. When that root system was destroyed, the drought and wind joined forces to cause disastrous soil erosion.

The blowing soil covered roads and created drifts that, in some places, were high enough to bury houses. Dust clouds, more than 1 mile (1.6 kilometer) high and as wide as the eye could see, blew across the land and were frequently dense enough to block out the Sun. Around 300 million tons (270 million metric tons) of topsoil blew away in a single dust storm in May 1934.

As the drought continued year after year, many people were forced to give up their dreams of farming in the area. In all, one-fourth of the people who lived in the Dust Bowl left the region. Many of them were lured to California by promises of fertile fields and plentiful work.

During and after the Dust Bowl tragedy, the federal government implemented a program to restore the land. Among the techniques used were replacing grasslands and planting trees, as well as introducing agricultural methods appropriate to the area. Those efforts were successful and, by the early 1940s, it was again possible to farm the land.

air mass: a large quantity of air throughout which temperature and moisture content is fairly constant.

cold front: the line behind which a cold air mass is advancing, and in front of which a warm air mass is retreating.

conservation tillage: the practice of leaving vegetation on fields during idle periods to protect the soil from erosion and trap moisture.

convection: the upward motion of an air mass or air parcel (a small volume of air that has a consistent temperature throughout, and experiences minimal mixing with the surrounding air) that has been heated.

cumulonimbus: tall, dark, ominous-looking clouds that produce thunderstorms. Also called thunderstorm clouds.

desert climate: the world's driest climate type, with less than 10 inches (25.4 centimeters) of rainfall annually.

desert pavement: hard, flat, dry ground and gravel that remains after all sand and dust has been eroded from a surface.

downdraft: a downward blast of air from a thunderstorm cloud, felt at the surface as a cool gust.

Dust Bowl: the popular name for the approximately 150,000 square-mile-area (400,000-square-kilometer-area) in the southern portion of the Great Plains region of the United States. It is characterized by low annual rainfall, a shallow layer of topsoil, and high winds.

dust devil: a spinning vortex of sand and dust that is usually harmless but may grow quite large. Also called a whirlwind.

dust storm: a large cloud of dust blown by a strong wind.

erosion: the wearing away of a surface by the action of wind, water, or ice.

Great Depression: the worst economic collapse in the history of the modern world. It began with the stock market crash of 1929 and lasted through the late 1930s.

haboob: a tumbling black wall of sand that has been stirred up by cold downdrafts along the leading edge of a thunderstorm or cold front. It occurs in north-central Africa and the southwestern United States.

harmattan: a mild, dry, and dusty wind that originates in the Sahara Desert.

khamsin: a hot, dry, southerly wind that originates on the Sahara and produces large sand and dust storms.

saltation: the wind-driven movement of particles along the ground and through the air.

shamal: a hot, dry, dusty wind that blows for one to five days at a time, producing great dust storms throughout the Persian Gulf.

simoom: a hot, dry, blustery, dust-laden wind that blows across the Sahara and the deserts of Israel, Syria, and the Arabian peninsula.

windbreak: row of trees or shrubs placed in a farm field to slow the wind and keep it from blowing away the soil.

A cloud of parched top soil picked up by winds and moving down a road near Boise City, Oklahoma, 1935. AP IMAGES.

The destruction of the prairie   In the early part of the twentieth century, farmers were encouraged to settle the Great Plains to grow wheat and other cereal crops. Land speculators claimed that the region was so fertile and the climate so dependable that "the rain would follow the plow." In the early years, plentiful rains produced bountiful crops.

With wheat in high demand, farmers plowed and planted acreages as large as their tractors could cover. As the amount of wheat being produced increased, the prices decreased. When farmers received less money for their grain, they tried to make up for the loss by increasing the size of their fields the following year. Thus increasingly more land was plowed and planted.

Certain agricultural practices added to the problem. Most farmers came to the plains from the Northeast and the Midwest, bringing with them farming techniques that had worked well in their former locations. One such method was to plant fields only every other season, allowing the fields to lie fallow—that is, without planting any crops—in between. During the fallow period, farmers frequently plowed the soil to uproot weeds, clean the surface of crop residues, and open the ground in the hopes of trapping moisture.

While that method may have worked well in the heartier soils in other parts of the country, it was a disaster in the Great Plains. The loosened, unprotected soil was made especially vulnerable to erosion by the high winds that came each year during the months of February, March, and April. The wind removed the finer silt and clay particles from the soil, leaving behind coarser particles of sand. With the fine particles went the soil's nutrients and organic matter, as well as its water storage capacity. The sandy soil that remained was of poor quality for growing crops.

Rain storms replaced by dust storms   A severe drought began in the eastern United States in 1930, and by the following year it had worked its way westward. As the drought progressed, dust storms, also called "black blizzards," grew more frequent and removed increasing amounts of topsoil. The storms made the sky turn dark in the middle of the day, stranded motorists, and stalled trains. Houses quickly filled with dust, and many people died from what doctors called "dust pneumonia (pronounced NEW-moan-ya)" when the dirt clogged their lungs. The number of major dust storms increased each year from 1932 to 1935.

The year 1934 saw the worst drought in the history of the United States. Seventy-five percent of the country suffered water shortages and twenty-seven states were severely affected. By the end of the year, some 35 million acres (14 million hectares) of farmland had been rendered useless for crop production. Soil erosion continued and in 1935 alone, an estimated 850 million tons (765 million metric tons) of topsoil blew off the southern plains. Yet even as crops refused to grow, farmers continued to plow and plant—hopeful that the rains would return. Instead, it only made things worse.

Black Sunday   On April 14, 1935, a day known as Black Sunday, the Dust Bowl experienced its worst dust storm of the era. Black Sunday

An Arkansas farmer and his sons in the Dust Bowl in 1936.
COURTESY FDR LIBRARY.

came at the end of weeks of dust storms, including a storm just two weeks earlier that had ruined 5 million acres (2 million hectares) of wheat. In the storm of April 14, visibility was reduced to zero, and people who were trapped outdoors suffocated. Thousands of livestock died in the fields. Robert Geiger, a reporter from the Associated Press, was on assignment in Guymon, Oklahoma, on that date. In his report filed April 15, Geiger coined the term "Dust Bowl"—and the term stuck. "Three little words achingly familiar on a Western farmer's tongue," wrote Geiger, "rule life in the dust bowl of the continent—'if it rains.'"

Black Sunday, which also happened to be Palm Sunday, the Sunday before Easter Sunday, began as a clear, sunny morning. Dust Bowl residents were grateful for the crisp blue skies, having grown weary of the hazy, dusty horizon. People flocked to country churches that morning, and after services families climbed into automobiles for Sunday drives.

By noon, the temperature had reached its high for the day—90°F (32°C). Shortly thereafter, the air began to cool rapidly. By midafternoon the temperature had dropped to just half of the noontime level. A huge, dark cloud appeared menacingly on the horizon.

To many people who saw the cloud approaching, it appeared as if the end of the world was upon them. The cloud extended from the ground to

Dust storm moving toward two houses during the Great Depression.

a height of more than 7,000 feet (2,135 meters), and as it moved across the land, it rolled over people, homes, and fields. Nothing escaped.

"The impact is like a shovelful of fine sand flung against the face," reported Avis D. Carlson in the *New Republic* following Black Sunday. "People caught in their own yards grope for the doorstep. Cars come to a standstill, for no light in the world can penetrate that swirling murk."

The New Deal provides relief   The economic disaster facing Dust Bowl farmers in the 1930s was made worse by the catastrophe plaguing the nation as a whole: the Great Depression. The Great Depression was the worst economic collapse in the history of the modern world. It began with the stock market crash in 1929 and lasted through the late 1930s. More than 15 million Americans, amounting to one-quarter of the workforce, found themselves unemployed. In better times, perhaps, the problems of the Dust Bowl farmers would have received more attention from the federal government. In the early 1930s, however, the farmers were just another down-and-out group.

When President Franklin Delano Roosevelt (1882–1945) took office in 1933, he began an enormous effort, known as the New Deal, to help the United States recover from the Great Depression. The New Deal

Eyewitness report: A first-hand account of the Dust Bowl

The following excerpts are from *Farming the Dust Bowl*, a memoir of the Dust Bowl years by Lawrence Svobida. Svobida was a wheat farmer in Kansas in the 1930s who had to leave his farm because of the years of drought and dust storms.

I did not yet know that the dry era had commenced, and that the spring of 1932 would see the creation of the dreaded Dust Bowl in our section of the Great Plains.

So, though my land lacked moisture, when seeding time came in September I drilled my wheat in dry ground.

...In January a foot of snow fell, but that was all the moisture we had, and it was not enough to make a crop. Some of my wheat came up, but it was thin, sickly looking stuff, with only two or three leaves to a plant.

...Most of my remaining wheat fell an easy prey to the first gales of February, and none of the wheat that was up in the region could long withstand the succeeding gales, which first chopped off the plants even with the ground, then proceeded to take the roots out. They did not stop there. They blew away the rich topsoil, leaving the subsoil exposed; and then kept sweeping away at the hardpan, which is almost as hard as concrete.

...Several times each day I anxiously scanned the sky. Time after time clouds formed and united together, and my hopes would rise; but no rain came, and my hopes would fade and die. I lived in suspense, looking, hoping, wishing—expecting rain that did not come.

...Throughout the fall and winter we had neither rain nor snow, and when the usual gales came in February they were worse in velocity and endurance than any I had previously experienced.

With the gales came the dust. Sometimes it was so thick that it completely hid the sun. Visibility ranged from nothing to fifty feet, the former when the eyes were filled with dirt which could not be avoided, even with goggles.... During a gale the dust would sift into the houses through crevices around the doors and windows, eventually to lie an inch or more deep all over the floors, and on tables, chairs, and beds.

...When I knew that my crop was irrevocably gone I experienced a deathly feeling which, I hope, can affect a man only once in a lifetime. My dreams and ambitions had been flouted by nature, and my shattered ideals seemed gone forever.... Fate had dealt me a cruel blow above which I felt utterly unable to rise. Season after season I had planted two, and sometimes three, crops. I had worked incessantly to gain a harvest, or to keep my land from blowing, and no effort of mine had proved fruitful. Words are useless to describe the sensation a human being experiences when the thin thread of faith snaps. I had reached the depths of utter despair.

...With my financial resources at last exhausted and my health seriously, if not permanently, impaired, I am at last ready to admit defeat and leave the Dust Bowl forever. With youth and ambition ground into the very dust itself, I can only drift with the tide.

Applicants fill the waiting room of the Works Progress Administration (WPA) office in Seattle, Washington, during the Great Depression. ©SEATTLE POST-INTELLIGENCER COLLECTION; MUSEUM OF HISTORY AND INDUSTRY/ CORBIS.

consisted of hundreds of social programs, building projects, and economic initiatives to get America back on its feet. Public works programs employed large numbers of people in a variety of construction and neighborhood improvement projects. One public works program, the Works Progress Administration (WPA), employed some 8.5 million people nationwide—including many Dust Bowl farmers. The WPA built hundreds of roads, bridges, buildings, parks, campgrounds, and other public facilities across the nation.

Beginning in 1933, the federal government provided help to Dust Bowl farmers with the Emergency Farm Mortgage Act, which made two hundred million dollars in loans available to farmers to help them keep their farms. The same year also saw the birth of the Agricultural Adjustment Administration, which paid farmers to reduce their acreage under cultivation in an effort to give the land a chance to stabilize. Toward the end of 1933, the Federal Surplus Relief Corporation (FSRC) purchased pigs from farmers who were struggling to feed their livestock. The FSRC slaughtered the animals and donated the meat to relief agencies. The FSRC also provided apples, beans, flour, and other products to agencies assisting struggling farmers.

A migrant family living in California in 1936.

In 1934 Congress approved the Frazier-Lemke Farm Bankruptcy Act, which limited the ability of banks to foreclose on farmers during drought or other times of misfortune. At the same time, Congress turned 140 million acres (56 million hectares) of federally owned land in the Dust Bowl into carefully monitored grazing districts to help prevent overgrazing and to stop erosion on those lands.

Migration from the Great Plains One consequence of the long drought was that many farmers were forced off their farms. During the 1930s, one out of four farmers in the Dust Bowl loaded up his family and belongings and left the region. This amounted to the largest migration in the history of the United States.

Of the 2.5 million people who left the Dust Bowl, about 200,000 ended up in California—lured by promises of plentiful jobs. There they found conditions that were in many ways as hopeless as those they had left. The migrants' miserable experience with California began on the highway at the border, where police tried to turn them away. An account of one farmer, published in *Collier's* magazine in 1935, reported a border agent stating: "California's relief rolls are overcrowded now. No use to come farther.... There really is nothing for you here.... Nothing, really nothing." The migrant farmer replied, "So? Well, you ought to see what they got where I come from."

Once the road-weary farmers made it to the rich agricultural land of the San Joaquin, they encountered new difficulties. Owners of enormous farming operations took advantage of the large number of people desperately seeking work and lowered wages. The Dust Bowl refugees were paid about one dollar a day to pick fruit and cotton. Out of that meager wage they were charged twenty-five cents a day to live in dilapidated shacks with no electricity or running water. Some farm owners operated company stores, at which they charged exorbitant rates for basic necessities. Since the migrants were typically living far from towns and many had no transportation, they had little choice but to patronize the company stores. As a result, many workers found that not only were they unable to save money, they actually became indebted to their employers.

Soil conservation measures adopted   In the early 1930s the federal government, through the Soil Erosion Service (SES), began implementing soil conservation measures on certain federal lands in the Great Plains. The SES's director, Hugh Bennett (1881–1960), came to be known as the father of soil conservation and pushed tirelessly for a greater commitment on the part of the federal government to save the land.

On April 27, 1935, Bennett was scheduled to address a Congressional committee about the need for enhanced soil conservation measures. Coincidentally, a dust storm on that day was reportedly heading eastward from northeastern New Mexico. Bennett believed that if the Washington lawmakers could experience the dust firsthand, they would be more likely to accept his proposals. Bennett stalled his presentation just long enough for the black blizzard to descend upon the capital. "This, gentlemen," stated Bennett in reference to the dust that dimmed the Sun, "is what I have been talking about." Bewildered legislators responded by declaring soil erosion "a national menace" and passing the Soil Conservation Act—legislation dedicated to the improvement of farming techniques.

Bennett lost no time putting into action a number of measures aimed at stabilizing the land. His grand plan was to put each acre to its best use—farmland, prairie, or forest—and to create specific land management plans according to the needs of every area. He first concentrated on returning seriously damaged land to grassland and planting windbreaks—lines of trees and shrubs—across windswept plains. He then focused on educating farmers about agricultural methods appropriate to the region. Farmers, reluctant to voluntarily change their practices, were paid one dollar per acre to go along with the federal conservation program.

By the end of the 1930s, conditions in the Dust Bowl were improving. As a result of conservation measures, the quantity of blowing soil had been decreased, and in the fall of 1939 the rains returned. Farming once again became possible in the Dust Bowl. Economic conditions also improved during the 1940s, driving up the price of wheat and other crops. As a result, farmers were able to make a living by cultivating smaller parcels of land. In 1943 Hugh Bennett summed up the hopeful spirit that had come over the region as follows: "If we are bold in our thinking, courageous in accepting new ideas, and willing to work with instead of against our land, we shall find in conservation farming an avenue to the greatest food production the world has ever known."

On the shelf: Dust Bowl migrants immortalized in *The Grapes of Wrath*

The anguish of the Dust Bowl years was captured by American writer John Steinbeck (1902–68) in his famous novel *The Grapes of Wrath*. This book tells the story of the Joads, a family of farmers forced to leave their land in Oklahoma. The Joads followed the promise of agricultural opportunity in California, only to face further hardships at the hands of ruthless farm owners. The novel opened the eyes of the nation to the plight of migrant farmworkers during the Great Depression.

The Grapes of Wrath won a Pulitzer Prize and a National Book Award, and was made into a movie in 1940. Steinbeck won the Nobel Prize for Literature in 1962. Following are excerpts from *The Grapes of Wrath:*

> When the truck had gone, loaded with implements, with heavy tools, with beds and springs, with every movable thing that might be sold, Tom hung around the place.... Behind him Ma moved about in the kitchen, washing children's clothes in a bucket; and her strong freckled arms dripped soapsuds from the elbows....
>
> She said, "Tom, I hope things is all right in California."
>
> He turned and looked at her. "What makes you think they ain't?" he asked.
>
> "Well—nothing. Seems too nice, kinda. I seen the han'bills fellas pass out, an' how much work they is, an' high wages an' all; an' I seen in the paper how they want folks to come an' pick grapes an' oranges an' peaches. That'd be nice work, Tom, pickin' peaches. Even if they wouldn't let you eat none, you could maybe snitch a little ratty one sometimes. An' it'd be nice under the trees, workin' in the shade. I'm scared of stuff so nice. I ain't got faith. I'm scared somepin ain't so nice about it."

> . . . Highway 66 is the main migrant road. 66—the long concrete path across the country, waving gently up and down on the map, from the Mississippi to Bakersfield—over the red lands and the gray lands, twisting up into the mountains, crossing the Divide and down into the bright and terrible desert, and across the desert to the mountains again, and into the rich California valleys.

> 66 is the path of a people in flight, refugees from the dust and shrinking land, from the thunder of tractors and shrinking ownership, from the desert's slow northward invasion, from the twisting winds that howl up out of Texas, from the floods that bring no richness to the land and steal what little richness is there....

> Two hundred and fifty thousand people over the road. Fifty thousand old cars—wounded, steaming. Wrecks along the road, abandoned. Well, what happened to them? What happened to the folks in that car? . . .

> "We ain't no bums," Tom insisted. "We're lookin' for work. We'll take any kind a work."

> The young man paused in fitting the brace to the valve slot. He looked in

amazement at Tom. "Lookin' for work?" he said. "So you're lookin' for work. What ya think ever'body else is lookin' for? Di'monds?..."

Tom said, "Back home some fellas come through with han'bills—orange ones. Says they need lots a people out here to work the crops."

The young man laughed. "They say they's three hunderd thousan' us folks here, an' I bet ever' dam' fam'ly seen them han'bills."

"Yeah, but if they don' need folks, what'd they go to the trouble puttin' them things out for?"...

"Look," the young man said. "S'pose you got a job a work an' there's jus' one fella wants the job. You got to pay 'im what he asts. But s'pose they's a hunderd men...wants that job. S'pose them men got kids, an' them kids is hungry. S'pose a lousy dime'll buy a box a mush for them kids. S'pose a nickel'll buy at leas' somepin for them kids. An' you got a hunderd men. Jus' offer 'em a nickel—why, they'll kill each other fightin' for that nickel.... That's why them han'bills was out. You can print a hell of a lot of han'bills with what ya save payin' fifteen cents an hour for fiel'work."

Scene from the 1940 movie, The Grapes of Wrath. © CORBIS.

Dangerous science: How dust storms happen

A dust storm begins when wind sweeps through dry areas that have loosened soils. The speed of the wind must be great enough to move larger particles, which then bump into tiny dust particles. There is a very shallow layer of calm air, extending only about 0.004 inch (0.01 centimeter) above the ground, which is unaffected by the wind. The tiny particles lay in that layer and are only stirred when they are struck by larger particles around them. For semiarid areas, such as Colorado and Arkansas, a sustained wind of 25 to 36 miles (40 to 58 kilometers) per hour is required to start a dust storm; for deserts, a sustained wind of 11 to 36 miles (18 to 58 kilometers) per hour is needed.

The strong wind sets in motion a process called saltation—the wind-driven movement of sand or soil particles along the ground. The moving particles bounce into other particles, sending them in motion. Some of the particles become airborne. When they fall back to the ground they strike other particles, knocking them upward and into the wind.

As the avalanche of particles continues its forward march, the whole surface of the soil gets blown into motion. While the larger particles remain close to the ground, the smaller particles get sent higher into the air and only make their way back down very slowly. The smallest particles get carried upward by air currents, rather than falling back to the ground, creating a cloud of dust. The dust moves along with the wind and is only deposited when the wind dies down, the particles become trapped by vegetation, or when rain begins to fall.

Haboobs   One type of sand-and-dust storm that occurs frequently in the deserts of the Sudan region of north-central Africa and in the southwestern region of the United States is the haboob (pronounced huh-BOOB). This word is taken from the Arabic word *habub,* which means "blowing furiously." A haboob is a tumbling, black wall of dust and sand that has been stirred up by cold downdrafts (downward blasts of air along the leading edge of a thunderstorm or a cold front, felt at the surface as cool gusts). The downdrafts strike the hot, dusty ground and force the surface air, as well as the top layer of sand and dust, upward. They create a wall of particles that may rise a mile or more above the ground, sometimes all the way to the base of the thunderstorm cloud, reducing visibility to near zero.

Haboobs generally last for thirty minutes to an hour and encompass areas ranging from several square miles to hundreds of square miles. They travel at speeds of about 30 miles (48 kilometers) per hour across short

A sand storm, or haboob, in North Khartoum, Sudan, 1906. ©HULTON-DEUTSCH COLLECTION/CORBIS.

spans or for great distances. Dust storms caused by the downdrafts of cold fronts—because of the vigorous winds and forceful lifting of air—tend to be the most intense form of haboobs. At the leading edge of a cold air mass, dust may be thrown as high as 23,000 feet (7,000 meters or 7 kilometers) into the air and transported for thousands of miles (kilometers).

Other types of desert dust and sand storms   Dust and sand storms occur frequently in deserts, due to the combination of loose soil and high winds. The windiness of deserts is primarily due to the heating of the surface. The temperature of the dry ground on a sunny day may be exceedingly hot, in some places more than 130°F (54°C). Air rises from the hot surface in a powerful convection (upward thrusting) flow, which sets surface winds blowing across the ground as cooler air rushes in from the surrounding area to take the place of the rising hot air. Wind speeds are greatest during the hottest part of the day and the hottest time of year.

As strong winds blow across a desert, they lift up and carry dust and sand. Dust and sand storms occur with the greatest frequency over western Africa, due to the harmattan (pronounced har-ma-TAHN; also spelled harmatan, harmetan, or hermitan)—a mild, dry, and dusty wind that originates in the Sahara. The harmattan is an easterly or northeasterly wind that produces dust and sand storms up to 20,000 feet (6,100 meters) high. More than 300 million tons (272 million metric tons) of reddish Saharan dust are transported westward across the continent each year, 100 million tons (91 million metric tons) of which are deposited into the Atlantic Ocean. Two or three times a year, Saharan dust travels 1,600 miles (2,574 kilometers) to Great Britain where it falls to the ground as a red precipitation that the locals call "blood rain."

Another hot, dry, southerly wind originating on the Sahara that produces large sand and dust storms is the khamsin (pronounced kahm-SENE). The khamsin forms over Libya and Egypt. When a storm is present to the west over Turkey, the khamsin blows dust over the northern tip of the Red Sea and into Saudi Arabia, Jordan, and Israel. The khamsin is a regular, annually occurring wind. Its name is the Arabic word for "fifty"; it blows for about fifty days straight, starting in mid-March. This dry wind brings air to the region that is hotter than 120°F (49°C) and has less than 10 percent relative humidity.

Great dust storms are produced each year throughout the Persian Gulf and the lower valley of the Tigris and Euphrates in Iraq by the shamal (pronounced shah-MALL). *Shamal* is the Arabic word for "left-hand" or "north." This hot, dry, and dusty wind from the northwest blows for periods lasting from one to five days at various times throughout the year. Once a year, typically in June and early July, the wind blows for forty days straight, at about 30 miles (50 kilometers) per hour, in what is known as the great shamal, or the forty-day shamal.

A dry, blustery, dust-laden wind called a simoom (pronounced si-MOOM) blows across North Africa and the Middle East, depositing its dust on Europe. The simoom, which often reaches temperatures of more than 130°F (54°C) and can cause heatstroke, is nicknamed the poison wind.

Consequences of dust storms

Dust storms can cause millions of dollars in damage to crops, roads, and buildings. Dust storms strip the land of the most fertile portion of the soil. Damage to soil results in a decline of productivity and a loss of income for farmers—often translating to higher food prices for consumers. Blowing soil can kill or damage seedlings, stunt the growth of vegetable crops, and introduce pathogens (microorganisms) that cause plant disease.

Water quality suffers during dust storms, as well. Dust settles into drainage ditches, and the tiny particles are difficult to remove entirely

Abandoned farm during the Oklahoma Dust Bowl. ©BETTMAN/CORBIS.

during the water treatment process. Dust storms also destroy wildlife habitat, causing certain populations of animals to either migrate in search of food or starve.

The sediment thrust into the air during dust storms reduces air quality and is harmful to human health. Inhalation of the particles is damaging to lungs and sinuses, and can trigger allergy attacks. During dust storms, hospitals and clinics report increased admissions for respiratory infections, cardiac disease, bronchitis, asthma, and pneumonia.

Dust storms, because of their reduction of visibility (sometimes to zero), pose a hazard to vehicles on the ground, in the air, and on the water. Dust enters and damages the inner workings of motor vehicles and other machines, as well.

Windblown dust, specifically the rubbing together of dirt particles, produces static electricity. During Dust Bowl storms, farmers saw balls of electricity traversing their barbed wire fences. The electric charge can

Dust devils

Dust devils, also called whirlwinds, are spinning columns of sand and dust. They typically arise on clear, hot, relatively calm days, over warm, dry surfaces such as deserts, plowed fields, or flat expanses of dirt. Dust devils form with less frequency along the leading, cold air/warm air boundary of a haboob (a tumbling black wall of sand that has been stirred up by cold downdrafts). Although dust devils bear a superficial resemblance to tornadoes, they are less destructive than their cloudy cousins and form by different processes.

The first step in the formation of a dust devil is when hot air rises forcefully from the surface by convection, creating a low pressure area at the surface. Next, surface winds converge (come together) to that point of low pressure. If there are horizontal layers of wind traveling at different speeds (a phenomenon called wind shear), it causes the rising air to spin about a vertical axis.

Dust devils are usually small, measuring less than 10 feet (3 meters) in diameter and less than 300 feet (91 meters) in height. They often last less than one minute. The largest dust devils reach a diameter of 100 feet (30 meters) and a height of 5,000 feet (1,524 meters) and last for twenty minutes or more. The wind speed in the largest dust devils may exceed 86 miles (138 kilometers) per hour.

A dust devil moving across the land in Kenya. JLM VISUALS.

Every year dust devils cause significant damage in the United States, including overturning mobile homes and tearing roofs off buildings. A large and long-lived dust devil can toss more than 50 tons (45 metric tons) of dust and debris up toward the sky.

cause dry material, such as withered crops and fence posts, to catch fire. It also alters the workings of electronic equipment; it can scramble radio broadcasts and short out car ignitions.

The human factor

Humans contribute to the formation of dust storms through improper agricultural practices and overgrazing cattle. This is particularly true in semiarid areas, such as the southern portion of the Great Plains. The topsoil there exists in a thin layer and is best suited for growing grass. Grass protects the soil above ground by reducing the force of the wind; underground, its roots anchor the soil in place. If the land is plowed for planting, or if cattle overgraze, the grass is removed and the soil's stabilization system is destroyed. If dry conditions then prevail (removing moisture—the remaining anchor for the soil), the soil can easily be blown away.

While erosion on the scale of the Dust Bowl has not recurred in the United States since the 1930s, erosion remains a serious problem in the Great Plains and in the western United States. The states most susceptible to this problem are Texas, Colorado, Nevada, and Montana. In 2000, almost five million acres of agricultural land in the United States experienced soil loss.

Technology connection

Soil scientists have developed several methods for reducing the incidence and intensity of dust storms, all of which involve the anchoring of the soil to prevent it from blowing away. On non-agricultural lands, such as seacoasts, steep slopes, and deserts, people plant sturdy grasses to prevent erosion. On agricultural lands, the practices used to prevent or lessen the effects of dust storms are similar to those used against drought.

One example of an erosion-combatting agricultural practice is the planting of rows of trees or shrubs, called windbreaks, at intervals throughout farm fields. Windbreaks, which run crossways to the direction that the wind usually blows, slow the wind and keep it from blowing away the soil. According to one study, a thin row of cottonwood trees is capable of reducing wind speed by one-third, dropping the speed from 15 miles (24 kilometers) per hour to 10 miles (16 kilometers) per hour. Trees also trap snow on the ground, thereby increasing the moisture content of the soil.

On the shelves: *Dust Bowl Diary*

Dust Bowl Diary, by Ann Marie Low, provides a first-hand account of what it was like to grow up during the Dust Bowl era of the late 1920s and early 1930s. The book is based on a diary that Low kept beginning in 1927, when she was fifteen years old and living on a farm in North Dakota. The book spans ten years and chronicles her life during the Dust Bowl and Great Depression.

"Many days this spring the air is just full of dirt coming, literally for hundreds of miles," Low writes in her April 25, 1934, entry. "It sifts into everything. After we wash the dishes and put them away, so much dirt sifts into the cupboards we must wash them again before the next meal. Clothes in the closets are covered with dust."

Through her personal account, Low offers a window into the social and economic conditions that characterized the era. *Dust Bowl Diary* also provides a rare and exciting opportunity to read about a major historical event from the perspective of a teenager.

Another strategy, called conservation tillage, is the practice of leaving stubble from the previous season's crop, or growing a cover crop, on fields during fallow (idle) periods. The vegetation left on fields protects the soil from erosion and traps moisture. Farmers also protect the soil by digging waterways in fields. The waterways keep soil from washing away during heavy rains, as well as catch and divert rainwater.

Strip plowing, terrace farming, and crop rotation are three more ways to guard against dust storms on agricultural lands. Strip plowing is the alternating of rows of wheat with rows of fast-growing, dense plants such as sorghum (pronounced SOAR-gum) or sudan grass. Terrace farming, which also aims to trap soil and water, involves the building of earthen terraces in fields as well as mixing rows of cereal crops, like wheat, with rows of grasses, shrubs, and trees. Crop rotation is the alternating use of a given field from year to year. A three-year cycle of crop rotation may involve, for example, using a field for wheat one year, then sorghum, and then letting it lie fallow—that is, without any planting.

A matter of survival

Dust storms, though of lesser intensity and frequency than during the 1930s, remain common occurrences in the western United States. A typical dust storm today lasts fifteen to twenty minutes. It either reduces visibility, causing a brownout, or blocks out all light, causing a blackout.

If you see a dust storm coming, immediately seek shelter indoors. Seal openings around doors and windows with wet towels. If you are stuck outdoors during a dust storm, turn your face away from the wind, and cover your mouth, nose, and eyes with a cloth.

If a dust storm approaches while you are traveling in your car, pull off the road as far as possible so other cars don't run into you. If you're on a highway shoulder, turn off your lights so that other drivers do not think you're on the road and drive up behind you. If a dust storm approaches, and you are not able to pull off the road, slow down and put on your flashing hazard lights. Exit the road as quickly as possible. Don't leave your car; it's easy to become disoriented and lose your way in a dust storm.

[*See Also* **Drought**]

For More Information

BOOKS

Allaby, Michael. *Droughts.* New York: Facts on File, Inc., 1998.

Andryszewski, Tricia. *The Dust Bowl: Disaster on the Plains.* Brookfield, CT: The Millbrook Press, 1984.

Knapp, Brian. *Drought.* Austin, TX: Steck-Vaughn Library, 1990.

Lancaster, Nicolas. "Geologic Work by Wind" in *Encyclopedia of Earth Sciences.* E. Julius Dasch, ed. New York: Macmillan Library Reference, 1996.

Prospero, J. M. "Dust Storm." *McGraw Hill Encyclopedia of Science and Technology.* New York: McGraw-Hill, 1997.

Stanley, Jerry. *Children of the Dust Bowl: The True Story of the School at Weedpatch Camp.* New York: Crown Publishers Inc., 1992.

Stewart, Gail B. *Drought.* New York: Crestwood House, 1990.

Svobida, Lawrence. *Farming the Dust Bowl: A First-Hand Account from Kansas.* Lawrence, KS: University Press of Kansas, 1986. (Originally published in 1940 by The Caxton Printers, Ltd.)

Walker, Jane. *Famine, Drought and Plagues.* New York: Gloucester Press, 1992.

Worster, Donald. *Dust Bowl: The Southern Plains in the 1930s.* New York: Oxford University Press, 1979.

Earthquake

An earthquake is a sudden shifting of masses of rock beneath Earth's surface. This motion releases enormous amounts of energy and sends out shock waves that cause the ground to shake. Geologists believe that no spot in the world is completely safe from earthquakes. The great internal forces of the planet are constantly changing the shape of Earth's surface. In fact, Earth has been resounding with earthquakes for more than four billion years.

Thousands of earthquakes occur each day. While not all of these earthquakes are significant, some are powerful enough to wreck cities and kill thousands of people. In the twentieth century alone, deadly earthquakes have claimed more than a million lives.

The 1906 San Francisco earthquake

On April 18, 1906, as the first rays of dawn began to spread across the sky, residents of San Francisco, California, were violently awakened as an earthquake shook the ground beneath the city. Most present-day geologists believe the earthquake, which came in two stages, measured 8.3 on the Richter scale. Other geologists believe the magnitude of the earthquake was slightly less, measuring about 7.8. (The Richter scale measures the magnitude of an earthquake or size of ground waves generated at the earthquake's source; a magnitude of 7.0 produces major damage, and a magnitude of 8.0 produces almost total damage. Every increase of one number on the Richter scale means a ten-fold increase in magnitude.)

Minutes after the earthquake struck, fires from broken gas and electrical lines began raging through the city. They burned uncontrollably for three days. Initial reports listed the number of dead as 700 to 800, but present-day research has led historians to conclude that more than 3,000 deaths were caused directly or indirectly by the earthquake and fires. Out of a population of 400,000, more than 200,000 people were injured and

251

WORDS TO KNOW

aftershock: ground shaking that occurs after the main shock of an earthquake.

asthenosphere: region of the mantle below the lithosphere, composed of partially melted rock.

continental drift: geologic theory that all continents were part of a single, original landmass before they slowly separated and gradually drifted apart.

convection current: circular movement of a gas or liquid between hot and cold areas.

crust: outermost layer of Earth, varying in thickness from 3.5 to 50 miles (5 to 80 kilometers).

epicenter: the point on Earth's surface directly above the focus of an earthquake, where seismic waves first appear.

fault: crack in Earth's surface where two plates or sections of the crust push and slide in opposite directions against one another.

fault creep: slow, continuous movement of plates along a fault, allowing pressure to be released.

focus: the underground starting place of an earthquake, also called the hypocenter.

foreshock: ground shaking that occurs before the main shock of an earthquake.

intensity: description of the physical damage caused by an earthquake.

liquefaction: the transformation of water-saturated soil into a liquidlike mass, usually by the action of seismic waves.

lithosphere: the rigid outermost region of Earth, composed of the crust and the upper part of the mantle.

magnitude: the power of an earthquake, as recorded by a seismograph, or seismometer.

mantle: thick, dense layer of rock that lies beneath Earth's crust. The mantle is about 1,800 miles (2,900 kilometers) thick and accounts for about 84 percent of Earth's volume.

modified Mercalli scale: scale developed by Italian seismologist Giuseppe Mercalli to measure the intensity of an earthquake based on the amount of vibration felt by people and the extent of damage to buildings.

plate tectonics: geologic theory that Earth's crust is composed of rigid plates that "float" toward or away from each other, either directly or indirectly, creating the major geologic features on the planet's surface.

Richter scale: scale developed by American seismologist Charles Richter that describes the amount of energy released by an earthquake.

seismic waves: vibrations that move outward from the focus of an earthquake, causing the ground to shake.

seismograph: instrument used to detect and measure seismic waves. Also known as a seismometer.

more than 250,000 were left homeless. Some 28,000 buildings were destroyed. The estimated total property damage from the earthquake and three-day fire was placed at more than 400 million dollars (in 1906 dollars).

Troops walking down Market Street after the 1906 San Francisco earthquake.
©BETTMANN/CORBIS.

A city's history is changed in one day   The area from present-day San Francisco south to Monterey Bay had been home to Native Americans for more than ten thousand years before the first Europeans arrived on the land. About forty culturally diverse native tribes (now known collectively as the Ohlone, a Miwok word meaning "western people") occupied this area when Spanish explorers and missionaries established a presidio (fortress) and a mission on the site of present-day San Francisco in 1776.

The Spanish settlement, named Yerba Buena, remained in Spanish hands until 1821, when it came under Mexican control. U.S. naval forces occupied the village in 1846 when the Mexican War (1846–48) broke out between the United States and Mexico. When the war ended in 1848, the United States gained control of the village and renamed it San Francisco.

At about the time the war ended, gold was discovered in California. The population of San Francisco was then about eight hundred. Two years later, because of the mad rush to find gold, the city's population had grown to some twenty-five thousand. California became linked to the east by the Pony Express (mail delivery system comprised of relay teams of men riding ponies between Missouri and California) in 1860, and by the first transcontinental railroad in 1869.

By the beginning of the twentieth century, San Francisco was a booming metropolis with an art museum, numerous universities, a

San Andreas Fault, California.
JLM VISUALS.

large commercial and fishing port, and a population of about 400,000. In just fifty years, it had become one of the largest cities in the United States. On April 18, 1906, however, San Francisco's rapid growth was brought to a halt, and the city's landscape and history were forever changed.

Lies on a fault A fault is a crack in Earth's surface where two plates (sections of the crust) meet. At the San Andreas Fault, on which the city of San Francisco is situated, the Pacific plate and the North American plate push past each other. The Pacific plate moves slowly to the northwest, while the North American plate moves equally slowly to the southeast.

The San Andreas Fault came into being about fifteen to twenty million years ago. The entire fault system forms a continuous narrow break in Earth's crust that runs more than 800 miles (1,287 kilometers) from northwest California south to the Gulf of California. The fault extends downward at least 10 miles (16 kilometers) into the planet's crust. On the surface, the fault appears as an area of crushed and broken rock measuring a few hundred feet to 1 mile (1.6 kilometer) wide.

The plates move at an average rate of about 2 inches (5 centimeters) per year. Rather than sliding smoothly past each other like oiled blocks, the plates make sudden, jerky movements. First one plate moves, then the other. Sometimes the plates lock against each other and are unable to move. Pressure builds up between them. After many years, perhaps centuries or more, the plates overcome the built-up pressure and suddenly move with great force. When that happens, a massive earthquake occurs. Such was the case in 1906 along the fault near San Francisco.

Awakening to a nightmare Before that fateful Wednesday morning in April, the Pacific and North American plates were locked, and pressure had been building along the northernmost section of the San Andreas Fault. At 5:12 AM local time, the internal forces on the fault finally broke free. Like a compressed spring that is suddenly released, the two sides of the locked fault abruptly tore the ground apart along a 290-mile (467-kilometer) stretch from San Juan Bautista to Cape Mendocino. The ground west of the fault shifted northward as much as 21 feet (6.4 meters) in places. Tremendous amounts of energy were released, and the earth shook violently. The epicenter of the earthquake—the point on Earth's surface directly above the focus, or the place where energy is first released—was near San Francisco.

The foreshock, an earthquake tremor that occurs before the larger main shock, lasted about twenty seconds. It was strong enough to be felt throughout the San Francisco Bay area. The main shock hit the area about twenty-five seconds later and lasted for almost one minute. The strong shaking, punctuated by fierce jolts, was felt from southern Oregon to southern California and as far east as Nevada.

Numerous buildings in San Francisco collapsed during the main shock. Many poorly constructed buildings situated on land that had been filled with loose stones and dirt sustained the worst damage. The newly constructed six million dollar city hall was ruined, and the Sonoma Wine Company building collapsed, spilling 15 million gallons (57 million liters) of wine.

Shaken from their slumber, many people ran into the streets dazed and horrified. Others were killed instantly or mortally wounded when bricks from nearby buildings or chimneys crashed through the roofs onto them. San Francisco Fire Department Chief Dennis T. Sullivan was one of the victims. While he was sleeping upstairs in a fire station, bricks from the California Hotel next door crashed through the roof of the station and fell on him.

Ten Deadliest Earthquakes 856–2004

Year	Place	Estimated Deaths
1556	Shanxi, China	830,000
2004	Sumatra (Indian Ocean)	280,000
1976	Tangshan, China	255,000
1138	Aleppo, Syria	230,000
856	Damghan, Iran	200,000
1920	Kansu (now Gansu), China	200,000
1927	Tsinghai, China	200,000
893	Ardabil, Iran	150,000
1293	Japan, Kanto	143,000

What people saw as they rushed onto the streets was a cityscape turned into a wasteland. American writer Jack London (1876–1916), who had been born in San Francisco and lived nearby, came into the city soon after the earthquake to witness the damage. His account appeared two weeks later in the national magazine *Collier's.*

London described the initial scene: "The streets were humped into ridges and depressions, and piled with the debris of fallen walls. The steel rails [of the streetcar and cable car tracks] were twisted into perpendicular and horizontal angles. The telephone and telegraph systems were disrupted. The great water mains had burst. All the shrewd contrivances and safeguards of man had been thrown out of gear by thirty seconds' twitching of the earth-crust."

Consumed by fire   Even those buildings left standing after the earthquake were not out of danger. Just minutes after the initial tremors waned, fires began to break out across the city. Downed electrical lines, toppled stoves, ruptured gas lines: all combined to set San Francisco ablaze.

Firefighters desperately sought ways to extinguish the raging fires. Hampered by a lack of water (most of the city's water mains had been ruptured), they decided to use dynamite to blow up damaged buildings in the paths of the fires. The idea was to create a firebreak by flattening the buildings and thus depriving the fire of fuel. The plan failed. Not only did

Most intense earthquakes in U.S. history

While the San Andreas Fault in California is well known as the source of many great earthquakes in the United States, the most intense earthquakes in the country over the past two hundred years occurred elsewhere. In the winter of 1811–12, three earthquakes centered on the New Madrid Fault in Missouri affected an area sixteen times larger than the 1906 San Francisco earthquake.

The three principal earthquakes that struck New Madrid, a city in southeastern Missouri on the banks of the Missouri River, took place on December 16, January 23, and February 7. Present-day scientists estimate that the quakes ranged in magnitude from 8.4 to 8.7 on the Richter scale. The intense ground vibrations caused by the main earthquakes and their many aftershocks bent trees until their trunks snapped, opened deep cracks in the soil, caused landslides on bluffs and low hills, created waves on the

Mississippi River that overturned many boats, and changed the elevation of land in the area by as much as 20 feet (6 meters). The last, and most intense, of the three earthquakes altered the course of the Mississippi River and created a depression in the northwest Tennessee landscape that filled with river water to become Reelfoot Lake.

Fortunately, few lives were lost because the area was sparsely populated. Seismic waves and their effects, however, were felt for thousands of miles. Stone and masonry buildings as far away as 155 miles (250 kilometers) suffered severe damage. Structural damage was recorded in Pittsburgh, Washington, D.C., and coastal South Carolina. The vibrations surprised people in Chicago and Detroit and even caused church bells to ring in Boston, some 1,100 miles (1,770 kilometers) away.

the dynamited buildings fail to stop the fires, but the explosions added to the inferno.

By mid-afternoon, one huge blaze had taken over the heart of the city. It had become so large and so hot that it began to create its own wind. Jack London, looking at the burning city from a boat anchored in San Francisco Bay, described the strange, dreamlike scene: "It was dead calm. Not a flicker of wind stirred. Yet from every side wind was pouring in upon the city. East, west, north, and south, strong winds were blowing upon the doomed city. The heated air rising made an enormous suck. Thus did the fire of itself build its own colossal chimney through the atmosphere."

The aftermath   The fires burned for three days. Sixty percent of the residential buildings in the city and the entire business district had burned. Almost 500 square blocks had been destroyed, and another thirty-two had partially burned. Overall, more than 2,590 acres (1,036 hectares), or about 4 square miles (10.4 square kilometers), had been ravaged by fire.

In the days following the earthquake and fires, hundreds of thousands of people fled San Francisco and the surrounding area. Most of those who remained were homeless but found shelter at makeshift camps set up around the city. Donated supplies poured in from all over the United States, staving off possible famine and more deaths.

Scientists predict that San Francisco may experience another massive earthquake midway through the twenty-first century. They base this estimate on data from the last 1,500 years indicating that major earthquakes occur along the San Andreas Fault about once every 150 years. Nonetheless, the area is prone to frequent, moderate-sized (yet damaging) earthquakes. The 1989 earthquake centered at Loma Prieta, 50 miles (80 kilometers) south of San Francisco, is one such example.

Recent events: Catastrophic earthquakes since 2000

Though many earthquakes occurred between the 2000 and 2005, the 2004 Indian Ocean earthquake and the 2005 Kashmir earthquake were especially destructive and deadly.

The Sumatra-Andaman earthquake of 2004   The Sumatra-Andaman earthquake, also known as the Indian Ocean earthquake, occurred on December 26, 2004. It was also one of the most powerful earthquakes on record. The event registered 9.0 on the Richter scale and was later upgraded to a magnitude between 9.1 and 9.3.

The Sumatra-Andaman earthquake struck off the coast of Indonesia, but its effects were far-reaching. The event is perhaps best remembered because it triggered a series of deadly tsunamis, or giant waves, which devastated countries that border the Indian Ocean. At the time of the earthquake, there was no reliable early warning system for Indian Ocean tsunamis, so the giant waves took people by surprise, battering coastal areas.

Casualties were especially high in Indonesia, Sri Lanka, India, and Thailand. When the waves hit, people were going about their business as usual. Tourists played on beaches, fisherman worked, and families went about their ordinary routines. People did not expect the giant waves that came ashore, destroying buildings and homes, and carrying debris like cars and construction materials farther inland. Well over 100,000 people

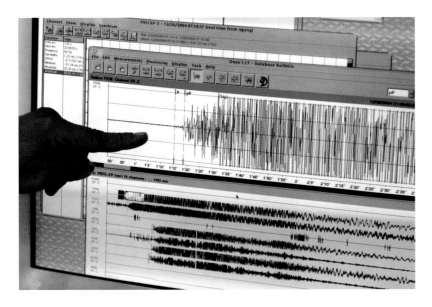

Seismograph showing the December 2004 Indian Ocean earthquake. © MAST IRHAM/ EPA/CORBIS.

died in Indonesia alone. The damage caused by the tsunamis displaced over a million people and caused billions of dollars worth of damage.

The destructive earthquake set records. The event created the longest fault rupture on record, creating an opening in Earth's seabed almost 800 miles long. The earthquake was also the longest-lasting on record with a duration of 500 to 600 seconds (about 10 minutes). By contrast, many small earthquakes last only one second. According to scientists, the average ground movement along the fault was at least 16.5 feet (5 meters). In some places, the ground moved as much as 20 feet.

Scientists say that the Sumatra-Andaman earthquake literally shook the entire planet. Scientists were able to detect movement from the event in every place in the world that seismic activity is measured. Thanks to new technology in earthquake measuring instruments, like global broad-band seismometers, scientists were able to measure the Sumatra-Andaman event with more precision than ever.

The destructiveness of the Sumatra-Andaman earthquake created widespread human suffering. This tragedy has motivated the scientific community to develop a reliable warning system for tsunamis in the Indian Ocean.

The Kashmir earthquake of 2005 Another historic and disastrous earthquake happened on October 8, 2005, in the Kashmir region of Pakistan.

This region is one of the most seismically active in the world. The 2005 earthquake had a magnitude of 7.6 on the Richter scale. It was the strongest earthquake on record in Pakistan. It was followed by a series of powerful aftershocks, measuring as much as 6.3 on the Richter scale. The epicenter of this powerful earthquake was about 60 miles north-northeast of Islamabad, Pakistan's capital.

The Kashmir earthquake was one of the most destructive of all time. In addition to causing widespread destruction, the earthquake killed almost 80,000 people. At least as many people were injured. The earthquake left three million people homeless just before the onset of the winter, which is bitterly cold and severe in the region, which includes parts of the Himalayan mountain range.

The gravest damage caused by the Kashmir earthquake was said to be in the village of Balakot, which is near the epicenter of the earthquake. Portions of the village, which is located on a hillside, literally slid down the hill. Most of the village was completely flattened by the earthquake. The residents of Balakot were among the millions displaced by the earthquake.

In addition to nearly decimating many mountain villages like Balakot, the Kashmir earthquake caused a number of landslides. These landslides cut off crucial thoroughfares across the mountains to the north of Islamabad. Because winter was coming, aid workers feared a second wave of deaths from the earthquake. They worried that people left homeless would die from exposure to the cold or from starvation. Fortunately, predictions that millions of displaced people would die turned out to be wrong. Many people were spared by a winter more mild than most. Aid agencies also found ways to transport food and supplies to isolated communities.

Still, the Kashmir quake devastated the region. Eyewitnesses reported that landslides continued well into the month of October, making mountain areas especially dangerous. Extensive farming infrastructure was destroyed, causing not only food shortages but also losses of livelihood.

Dangerous science: What causes earthquakes?

The answer to what causes earthquakes is found in both the structure of Earth's surface and the forces that rage inside the planet. The interior of Earth—from the planet's center to its surface (a distance of about 3,975

A Kashmiri man sits at a road side overlooking the devastation caused by an earthquake in the village of Kamsar, Kashmir, in 2005. ©AHMAD MASOOD/ REUTERS/CORBIS.

miles [6,395 kilometers])—is divided into layers, defined by their material composition. The core, at the center of the planet, is composed of a solid inner portion about 780 miles (1,300 kilometers) thick and a liquid outer portion about 1,380 miles (2,220 kilometers) thick. Surrounding the core with a depth of about 1,800 miles (2,900 kilometers) is the mantle. The crust, or surface layer surrounding the mantle, varies in thickness from 5 to 25 miles (8 to 40 kilometers).

The mantle is divided into two sections. The upper section, directly below the crust and about 40 miles (65 kilometers) thick, is solid. The section beneath it is soft, or partially melted. The crust and the rigid section of the mantle together compose what geologists call the lithosphere (pronounced LI-thuh-sphere). The soft section of the mantle is called the asthenosphere (pronounced ass-THEE-nuh-sphere).

Most geologists believe that convection currents (circular movements of fluid between hot and cold areas) in the asthenosphere are the driving force behind earthquakes and other movements on the surface of the planet. The heat energy at the center of Earth—where temperatures are estimated to exceed 9,900°F (5,480°C)—is carried to the surface by convection currents. As they near the crust, the currents cool and sink back toward the center to

Reports from the past: Prehistoric earthquakes point to the future

In July 1998, two scientists published a study in the journal *Science* in which they asserted that there had been at least two giant prehistoric earthquakes near present-day Los Angeles. The scientists estimated that the earthquakes occurred within the last 15,000 years on the Sierra Madre Fault, which runs 12 miles (19 kilometers) north of the city. It was previously believed that earthquakes had not occurred on that fault.

The scientists, by measuring different layers of soil in the faulted region, determined that the ground had moved more than 16.5 feet (5 meters) on average during the ancient tremors. Based on that figure, they estimated that the earthquakes had ranged in strength from 7.2 to 7.6 on the Richter scale.

The scientists made no predictions of future earthquakes, merely pointing out that it was possible for an earthquake to eventually strike the city. If an earthquake were to occur today in the same place as the prehistoric earthquakes, the scientists reasoned, strong tremors would be sent directly into the heart of Los Angeles. Such an earthquake would cause immense destruction in the heavily populated city.

be heated once again. The pressure created by the action of these currents is released on Earth's surface through volcanoes and earthquakes.

Plate tectonics Plate tectonics is the geologic theory that Earth's crust is made up of rigid plates that float on the surface of the planet. (Tectonics comes from the Greek word meaning "builder.") The plates make up the lithosphere and float on the underlying asthenosphere. There are seven major plates and several smaller ones that are in constant contact with each other. When one plate moves, it causes other plates to move. The movement of the plates toward or away from each other either creates the major geologic features, such as mountain ranges or faults, at Earth's surface.

Plate tectonics is a relatively new scientific theory. This theory is built on the idea of continental drift, introduced in the 1920s by German geophysicist Alfred Wegener (1880–1930). Wegener believed that all continents were part of a single, original landmass—a supercontinent he called Pangaea (pronounced pan-JEE-ah)—before they gradually separated and drifted apart. His concept was based on the fact that several of the planet's continents seem to fit together like pieces in a jigsaw puzzle. This is particularly apparent when examining the eastern coast of South America and the western coast of Africa. Wegener, however, could not provide a convincing argument as to what made the continents shift around Earth's surface.

That question was answered by the theory of plate tectonics. The theory states that tectonic plates, moving about Earth's surface in response to pressure beneath them, interact with each other in one of three ways: they converge (move toward one another), diverge (move away from one another), or transform (slide past one another). The boundaries where plates meet are known as plate margins.

Faults As two rock plates slide past one another, a crack or fault develops at the plate margin. Most earthquakes occur along faults (also called fault lines). The principle types of faults are normal, reverse, and strike-slip. A normal fault forms when two plates are being pulled or stretched apart. A reverse fault, in contrast, forms when two plates are being pushed together—the compression forces one plate up and over the other. A strike-slip fault, the most common type of fault, forms when the edge of one plate grinds against the edge of another as it slips sideways. The San Andreas Fault, the best known fault in the continental United States, is a strike-slip fault.

When plates along a fault move slowly and continuously, allowing pressure to be released, the movement is called fault creep. More often, however, the lower parts of the plates move slowly and continuously along the soft portion of the mantle while the upper parts of the plates,

Alfred Wegener.
©BETTMANN/CORBIS.

where the surface is solid rock, remain locked in position. Such a configuration causes stress to build up in the crust. When that stress becomes greater than the forces holding the surface plates in position, the crust can rupture. The stored energy is then released through ground vibrations—better known as earthquakes. There are more than one million earthquakes a year around the planet, although most are too faint to be noticed.

Earthquake zones On Earth, about 90 percent of earthquakes occur around the outer rim of the Pacific Ocean. This area is where the edges of the Pacific plate, the portion of the Earth's crust that lies beneath the Pacific Ocean, come in contact with several other plates. On its western side, the Pacific plate slides beneath the Eurasian and Indo-Australian plates. Along its northeastern side, the Pacific plate comes up against the North American plate. The north-central edge of the Pacific plate rides above the Nazca plate (located between the Pacific plate and the South American plate).

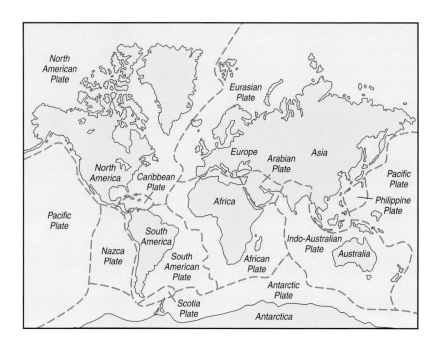

Plates composing Earth's crust.

Not only does the outer rim of the Pacific Ocean have frequent earthquakes, but it also contains three-quarters of the world's volcanoes. For this reason, this circular area is also known as the Ring of Fire (or Circle of Fire).

Seismic waves: The motion of earthquakes   Vibrations transmitting the shock of an earthquake are called seismic (pronounced SIZE-mik) waves. These waves travel both underground and along Earth's surface in all directions, like ripples from a stone dropped in a pond. The underground area where energy is first released, triggering an earthquake, is called the focus (or hypocenter). The focus may be as far as 430 miles (700 kilometers) beneath Earth's surface. The point on the surface directly above the focus is called the epicenter.

When an earthquake occurs, two main classes of seismic waves are generated. The first class waves, called body waves, are generated below ground, from the source of the earthquake, and travel to the surface. Body waves consist of P (primary) waves and S (secondary) waves. The P waves travel fastest, up to 4 miles (6.4 kilometers) per second, and are the first waves to reach the surface. They stretch and compress the rock in their path and cause the ground to move vertically (upward). P waves release their energy to the atmosphere, resulting in the common thundering or rumbling sound associated with earthquakes.

S waves travel at about half the speed of P waves, or 2 miles (3.2 kilometers) per second. They move from side to side as well as upward, causing the ground to move horizontally as well as vertically. For this reason, S waves are far more destructive to buildings than are P waves.

S and P body waves combine near the epicenter to form surface waves or L (long) waves, which travel along Earth's surface. Although surface waves move slightly more slowly than body waves—less than 2 miles (3.2 kilometers) per second—they cause greater damage. Surface waves can set off avalanches, landslides, and tsunamis.

Seismic waves can travel great distances. For instance, in late 1811 and early 1812 a series of intense earthquakes hit the United States near New Madrid, Missouri. Vibrations could be felt more than 1,000 miles (1,600 kilometers) away. Although waves lose energy as they travel, they can still cause major destruction as they ripple outward.

Experiment: Understanding plate tectonics

Earth's crust is made up of large tectonic plates. These plates are always moving. They move slowly, but they move with incredible force. To understand what happens when plates move into each other, try this experiment. Get a sheet of newspaper, and find a large, hard, flat surface, either a table or the floor, where you can spread the newspaper flat. Put your palms down on the newspaper about a foot apart and slowly push them together. The newspaper will crumple and fold upward in the middle. When tectonic plates fold upward, mountains are created. When they crumple together, earthquakes are the result.

Aftermath: What are the effects of earthquakes on Earth and its inhabitants?

Great earthquakes leave telltale signs in the surface of Earth, especially in the area around the epicenter. A horizontal or vertical change in the ground level can often be seen near a fault. The most dramatic change is the creation of a scarp, or cliff. Depending on the type of rock and the amount of uplift caused by the earthquake, a scarp may be up to 1 mile (1.6 kilometer) tall.

Earthquakes can also produce fissures, or long cracks, in the ground. Often the ground on one side of a fissure is uplifted several inches or even several feet. In addition to being moved vertically, the ground on one side of a fissure can also be moved horizontally. One example of vast changes in ground level occurred in southern Alaska on March 27, 1964. On that date, an earthquake measuring 8.6 on the Richter scale struck the area,

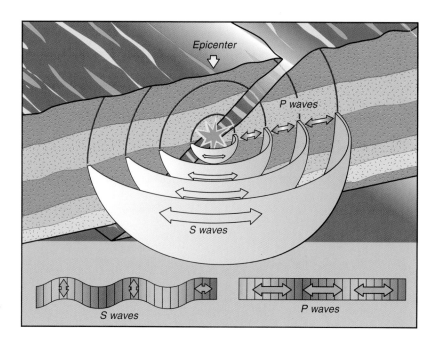

Action of seismic
waves.

permanently resculpting 77,220 square miles (200,000 square kilometers) of land surface. Almost 620 miles (1,000 kilometers) of coastline
from Kodiak Island to Prince William Sound was either uplifted or
lowered. In some places, the vertical uplift was as much as 36 feet (11
meters); in others, the subsidence, or lowering of ground level, was as
much as 7 feet (2 meters).

If a fissure occurs on a hill, it may set off a landslide. Landslides or
mud slides are rapid downhill movements of soil and rock. These slides
may encompass whole sections of a hill or mountain. During the landslide, the loosened soil and rock rushes down the slope, often destroying
everything in its path before finally coming to rest at the bottom of the
slope.

Underground structures such as springs and wells may be disturbed
by earthquakes. Springs may stop flowing, either temporarily or permanently, and new springs may form. The water in wells may be muddied or
its level changed. All of these effects can occur even at a great distance
from the epicenter of an earthquake. An extremely intense earthquake
may even force water, mud, and sand out of the ground, forming what are
called earthquake fountains and sand blows.

Pre-Renaissance artwork destroyed by earthquakes

Priceless frescoes attributed to Florentine painters Giotto (c.1266–1337) and Cimabue (c.1240–c.1302) were severely damaged when two earthquakes struck central Italy within hours of each other on September 26, 1997.

The earthquakes, which measured 5.5 and 5.6 on the Richter scale, killed eleven people and caused damage to nearly 1,500 buildings. The first earthquake struck at 2:33 AM local time. Its epicenter was close to the town of Foligno in Umbria, a region dotted with historic towns. The second earthquake struck some nine hours later. Tremors from both earthquakes were felt in Rome, more than 62 miles (100 kilometers) away.

Frescoes are paintings made on damp plaster walls. When the plaster dries, the painting becomes fixed to the wall. The frescoes by Giotto and Cimabue were part of the walls and ceiling of the thirteenth-century Basilica of San Francesco in Assisi, one of early Christianity's most important shrines. A renowned tourist attraction, the basilica is famous for its twenty-eight frescoes depicting the life of Francis of Assisi (c.1182–1226), founder of the Franciscan religious order.

The first earthquake caused deep cracks in many of the precious frescoes. Just as friars and structural experts were inside inspecting this damage, the second earthquake struck, causing an even greater tragedy. Huge sections of the vaulted ceiling of the basilica collapsed, killing four people and destroying many of the frescoes.

On November 28, 1999, just over two years after the earthquakes struck, a commemorative mass was held to reopen the church. The bell tower, the vault sections, and some of the frescoes had been repaired or reattached. Restorers estimated it would take at least another two years before other damaged frescoes, including Cimabue's *St. Matthew* and Giotto's *St. Jerome*, would be reassembled.

What makes earthquakes deadly? The damage created by an earthquake is most evident in human-made structures. An earthquake is more likely to cause injuries, fatalities, and damage the closer the epicenter is to a populated area. Earthquakes occurring in crowded cities leave behind buckled and broken sidewalks and streets, downed trees and power lines, and collapsed homes and buildings.

What usually kills people in an earthquake is not the earthquake itself, but the collapse of buildings, roads, and other structures. The greatest destruction is brought about, often miles away from the epicenter of an earthquake, through the process of liquefaction (pronounced li-quh-FAC-shun). When earthquake vibrations encounter layers of loosely packed soil containing water, the vibrations cause the particles of soil to lose contact with one another. This allows the water to bubble through, transforming the ground into a watery mass resembling quicksand.

Kobe earthquake of 1995

The largest earthquake to hit Japan in the last half of the twentieth century occurred on January 17, 1995. At 5:46 AM local time, an earthquake measuring 7.2 on the Richter scale struck the region of Kobe and Osaka in south-central Japan. The region includes Kobe, Japan's sixth largest city and the world's sixth largest port, with a population of some 1.5 million. The Kobe earthquake, dubbed the Great Hanshin Earthquake by the Japanese media, killed more than 5,500 people and injured 25,000 others. More than 300,000 people were left homeless. The Kobe earthquake was the deadliest natural disaster in Japan since 1923—the year that the Great Kanto Earthquake killed about 140,000 people.

The epicenter of the Kobe earthquake was located about 20 miles (32 kilometers) south of the city of Kobe near Awaji Island. The minor strike-slip fault on which the earthquake occurred runs from Awaji Island through Kobe. The earthquake caused the ground to move 7 inches (18 centimeters) horizontally and 4 inches (10 centimeters) vertically—the greatest ground displacement ever recorded in Japan. In the twenty-four hours after the main shock, 716 aftershocks were recorded.

The Kobe earthquake damaged or destroyed one out of every five buildings in the area, totaling more than 180,000 buildings. The violent ground shaking, which lasted for about twenty seconds, caused an estimated damage of about 147 billion dollars (U.S.).

Damage occurred throughout a 62-mile (100-kilometer) radius from the epicenter. This area encompassed the cities of Kobe, Osaka, and Kyoto, with Kobe being the most severely affected. Kobe, like much of modern urban Japan trying to keep up with a growing population, was built on very soft soil and landfills. The worst damage occurred near the waterfront where severe liquefaction took place, causing industrial buildings to sink and crumble. Ninety percent of the port's 187 berths were destroyed, and most large cranes along the waterfront were either damaged or destroyed.

Major utilities were severely disrupted in Kobe and surrounding cities. At one point, almost one million households were without electrical power, another 800,000 households lacked gas, and some 250,000 telephone lines were disconnected. Severed gas lines started fires that burned for days. Approximately 150 fires broke out in Kobe and surrounding areas in the hours immediately following the earthquake. Firefighters, hampered by a lack of water because of thousands of breaks in the water line system, were ill-equipped to fight the blazes. Streets clogged

Structures and roads built on this type of soil cannot be supported by this liquid mixture and thus sink or slide from their foundations.

Another serious consequence of earthquakes is fire. Broken gas lines, downed electrical wires, and overturned stoves and heaters start many fires (as was the case in the 1906 San Francisco earthquake). Because

with collapsed buildings and traffic congestion also blocked firefighters' efforts.

Houses built in the style of traditional Japanese architecture readily collapsed, killing their inhabitants. Heavy roofs composed of thick mud or tile fell as the thin walls supporting them buckled. Other structures throughout the city were also destroyed by the earthquake. Railway lines were twisted and bent, and train cars were thrown like toys. Elevated portions of the area's highway system collapsed or caved in. Impassable roads, bridges, and rails slowed the arrival of aid from nearby cities. In the period immediately after the earthquake, the only way of transporting emergency supplies was by bicycle or on foot.

The Kobe earthquake hit when most people were asleep. Had it come later in the day—when people filled trains, freeways, and sidewalks—the death toll would have been far higher.

A section of Kobe, Japan, demolished by the 1995 earthquake. ©MICHAEL S. YAMASHITA/CORBIS.

water mains and streets are damaged at the same time, the water needed to put out the fires is unavailable. In a populated region, the damage caused by fires frequently exceeds that caused by the ground shaking.

A secondary effect of an earthquake that occurs under the ocean is a tsunami (pronounced tsoo-NAH-mee), also called a tidal wave. A tsunami

Turkey's earthquakes of 1999

One of the deadliest earthquakes of the twentieth century hit northwest Turkey on August 17, 1999. At 3:02 AM local time, a violent tremor measuring 7.4 on the Richter scale shook the ground for forty-five seconds. The epicenter of the earthquake was located near the city of Izmit, 55 miles (88 kilometers) east of Istanbul. Almost half Turkish population lived in the area affected by the earthquake. When it was over, nearly 76,000 buildings had collapsed, an estimated 17,500 people were killed and more than 33,000 others injured. Almost 500,000 were left homeless. The Turkish government, which called the natural disaster one of the greatest in Turkish history.

Turkey lies atop some of the world's most unstable geology. The North Anatolian fault runs through the densely populated, industrial area of northern Turkey. This fault is a small slab of crust that marks the boundary between the Arabian plate to the south and the larger Eurasian plate to the north. Between the two plates lies the relatively small Turkish microplate, on which most of the country of Turkey is located. As the Arabian plate moves slowly northward, it pushes the Turkish microplate to the west relative to the Eurasian plate at a rate of about 1 inch (2.5 centimeters) per year. At times, the microplate sticks, then jerks free with great energy. This occurred on August 17.

The North Anatolian fault is more than 800 miles (1,287 kilometers) long and 10 miles (16 kilometers) deep. It is a perfect example of a strike-slip fault, where the ground moves side to side. After the August 17 earthquake, geologists measured the North Anatolian fault and found that in some places one side of the fault had shifted more than 12 feet (3.7 meters) relative to the other side.

Earthquakes are common in geologically unstable Turkey. According to historians, over the last 5,000 years major earthquakes have shaken northern Turkey about once every 175 years. Seven destructive earthquakes have occurred along the North Anatolian fault since 1939, the year in which an earthquake struck the eastern province of Erzincan and killed 30,000 people. Since then, the locations of the earthquakes along the fault have moved progressively westward.

The earthquake on August 17 was the most powerful to strike the area since 1939. Lives and buildings were destroyed up to 200 miles (322 kilometers) from the epicenter. Tremors from the earthquake were felt as far east as Ankara and across parts of the Balkans.

In central Istanbul, the majestic museums and historic mosques suffered no visible damage. In areas on the outskirts of the city, home to some twelve million people, newly built apartment complexes crumbled. In some places to the southeast of Istanbul, the destruction was nearly total.

is set in motion by a vertical shift in the ocean floor, which pushes the water ahead of it. The vertical shift generates waves that can travel across the ocean with speeds of 250 to 500 miles (400 to 800 kilometers) per

Rescue teams representing thirty-eight international organizations and forty-two countries arrived in the country shortly after the disaster. But many areas in desperate need of help received nothing for days, forcing the living to dig through the rubble with their bare hands in search of their family members, friends, and neighbors. Smashed sewer lines and a lack of fresh water and portable toilets raised the risk of the spread of infectious diseases among the hundreds of thousands of people left homeless by the earthquake.

On November 12, an earthquake measuring 7.2 struck the northwestern town of Duzce just after nightfall. Located in a hilly region about 115 miles (185 kilometers) east of Istanbul, Duzce was on the eastern fringe of the region hit by the August 17 earthquake. Hundreds of thousands of survivors from the first disaster were still living in tents in the rainy winter weather when the new earthquake struck. The Duzce earthquake lasted for thirty seconds, cutting communication lines and crumbling the main road leading into the town. More than 5,100 people were injured and more than 750 buildings were destroyed. The death toll exceeded 700.

Earthquake damage to a Turkish mosque, 1999. ©SERGEI CHIRIKOV/EPA/CORBIS.

hour. Tsunamis start out small and grow larger as they near land. It is typical for a large tsunami to measure 60 to 100 feet (18 to 30 meters) in height by the time it crashes onto land.

Earthquakes usher in year 2001

Within the first twenty-six days of 2001, major earthquakes struck two locations at opposite ends of Earth. The first quake shook the tiny Central American nation of El Salvador on January 13, and the second quake hit western India thirteen days later.

Measuring 7.6 on the Richter scale, El Salvador's earthquake killed some 700 people, injured more than 2,000 people, and left 65,000 families homeless. Damages totaled 1.5 billion dollars—about half of the gross earnings of all Salvadorans.

El Salvador's earthquake affected the capital city, San Salvador, and villages in the countryside alike. A large portion of the casualties occurred in Las Colinas, a suburb of San Salvador. A cluster of homes at the base of a hill there were buried under a wall of soil and mud that collapsed in an earthquake-triggered landslide. (The removal of trees from the hillside to make room for a coffee plantation and luxury homes was considered partially to blame for the landslide.) San Francisco Javier and San Augustin, both about 100 miles southeast of the capital, were representative of outlying towns in which virtually every building, most made of adobe walls and tin roofs, was reduced to rubble.

India's earthquake, a 7.9 on the Richter scale, had far greater consequences than El Salvador's. The death toll in India exceeded seventeen thousand, there were more than sixty thousand injuries, and one million people were left homeless. The earthquake, India's worst in half a century, occurred at about 9 o'clock in the morning on Republic Day (a national holiday honoring the Indian constitution).

The epicenter of the earthquake was below the heavily populated state of Gujarat, near the border with Pakistan. Buildings in cities throughout Gujarat, constructed without following earthquake-proof building codes, teetered and fell or collapsed in heaps. The hardest-hit city, Bhuj, lost 6,000 of its 150,000 residents and its hospital. Not a single building in Bhuj escaped without serious damage. In the town of Anjar, 400 children marching in a Republic Day parade were buried alive by debris from tumbling houses and high-rise buildings.

Throughout the region, the earthquake caused water supplies to become contaminated; destroyed roads, bridges, and railroad tracks; and downed telephone and power lines. The destruction not only made it hard for survivors to find food and water, but it made it difficult for relief workers with needed supplies to reach affected areas.

The human factor: How do people contribute to earthquake damage?

The most obvious way that people contribute to earthquake destruction is by building cities and towns within earthquake zones (areas situated on or near faults and other plate boundaries). Because scientists have identified these zones only within the last one hundred years, most cities were built with no knowledge of the danger. Complicating matters, wetlands and other moist lowland areas around many cities have been filled in with soil to create more living space. These filled-in areas are highly prone to liquefaction and destruction during earthquakes.

Along with ground instability and the possibility of liquefaction, the design of many buildings makes them susceptible to earthquake damage. Structures that are insufficiently braced or not tightly secured to their foundations can be damaged easily by earthquakes. The materials used to construct the buildings is another factor. For instance, wood is more flexible than brick and cement; therefore, wood-frame buildings are better equipped to withstand ground motion. Brick and cement structures often fracture and collapse during large earthquakes.

Further, some scientists said that human development and coral mining created conditions that worsened the impact of the Sumatra-Andaman earthquake. That 2004 earthquake, whose epicenter was in the Indian Ocean, triggered massive tsunamis that pulverized many countries that border that ocean. Normally, a coral reef acts as a natural barrier between the land and powerful ocean waves. When a reef is compromised or destroyed, there is no barrier to protect the land. Thus, some scientists think that the tsunami that resulted from the Sumatra-Andaman earthquake was taller and more powerful in areas where reefs had been compromised.

Artificial earthquakes? Scientists have recently begun exploring the occurrence of artificial or human-made earthquakes, such as those caused by quarry blasts or other large explosions. Another possible trigger of earthquakes is the underground detonation (for the purpose of testing) of large nuclear bombs. The tremors generated by this type of explosion are strong enough to be felt more than 100 miles away from the testing site. It is therefore plausible that such tremors could trigger the release of built-up pressure between two nearby plates, resulting in an earthquake.

The underground storage of hazardous liquid wastes is yet another problem. (Wastes deemed hazardous are those detrimental to human health or the environment because, for example, they catch fire at low temperatures, are extremely acidic, or undergo violent physical and/or chemical changes when mixed with water. Such wastes must be disposed of in accordance with strict standards developed by the Environmental Protection Agency.) Scientists believe that improper underground disposal of hazardous wastes may have caused an earthquake beneath northeastern Ohio on January 31, 1986. For the twelve years before that date, hazardous liquid wastes had been disposed of in two underground wells located almost 1.3 miles (2 kilometers) below ground. A total of about

350 million gallons (1.3 billion liters) of hazardous waste had been pumped into the wells. The pressure created by that volume may have ruptured the surrounding rock, causing cracks that reached an area where tectonic pressure had been building up. Whatever the cause, an earthquake measuring 4.9 on the Richter scale rocked this area in Ohio.

Technology connection: Measuring and predicting earthquakes

From the beginning of recorded history, people have tried to explain, predict, and measure earthquakes. Ancient people believed that the movement of various animals such as giant catfish, snakes, spiders, or turtles that lived beneath Earth's surface created earthquakes. One of the first people to attempt to explain the action of earthquakes based on natural phenomena was Greek philosopher Aristotle (384–322 BCE). He believed that winds within the planet caused shaking at the surface.

The first known earthquake-measuring device was invented by Chinese scholar and poet Zhang Heng (78–139) in the second century CE. The device, now called a seismoscope, is a huge bronze vase measuring 6 feet (1.8 meters) in diameter. Eight dragon heads are sculpted around the top. In the mouth of each dragon is a small bronze ball. Directly below each dragon head sits a bronze frog. Inside the vase, each dragon head is attached to a bar, which connects to a single pendulum (a hanging object that freely swings back and forth) in the middle of the vase. The pendulum swings from the movement of even the slightest tremor. When the pendulum swings, it pulls back one of the bars. The dragon's mouth opens, and the ball drops into the open mouth of the bronze frog directly below. The frog holding the ball indicates from which direction the tremor came.

Present-day scientists measure an earthquake's power by two standards: intensity and magnitude. While the intensity of an earthquake is determined by the amount of damage caused, magnitude is measured by using seismographs, also known as seismometers, or other devices that detect ground movement. Intensity is a measure of an effect; magnitude is a measure of released energy.

Seismology   Scientists use an instrument called a seismograph, or seismometer, to measure the waves caused by an earthquake. A seismograph consists of a heavy weight or pendulum hanging over a constantly revolving drum wrapped with recording paper. Attached to the end of the pendulum, with its tip touching the paper, is a recording pen or

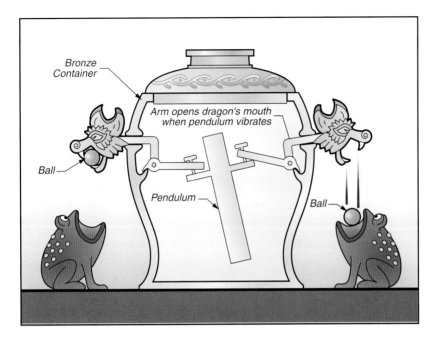

Illustration of an ancient seismoscope.

needle. When an earthquake occurs, the seismic waves cause the pendulum to swing, and the pen records that motion on the paper. The bigger the seismic wave, the larger the swing of the pendulum, and the wider the zigzag line made by the pen on the paper. Today, the motion of the pendulum can also be recorded as digital data on a computer.

Seismographs, or seismometers, are usually placed underground in deep holes away from the artificial vibrations caused by cars, airplanes, and other modern machinery. In 1931, only 350 seismographic stations existed around the world to measure earthquakes. By 2000 there were more than 4,000 stations recording data. That data is transmitted via satellite and computer to scientific institutions around the world.

The most recent seismographic technology includes the broadband seismometer, which is able to record a broad range of frequencies. These devices have allowed scientists to collect even more specific data on recent earthquakes like the 2004 Sumatra-Andaman earthquake and the 2005 Kashmir earthquake. This electronic device confines a small mass between electrical forces. When the Earth moves, the device measures how much force is required to hold the mass steady.

Mercalli scale In 1902 Italian seismologist Giuseppe Mercalli (1850–1914) developed a scale to compare the surface effects of

A scientist monitors Earth movements using a seismograph. ©REUTERS/CORBIS.

earthquakes. Mercalli's measurement of earthquake intensity was based not on scientific measurement but on the damage done to buildings. Updated in 1931 by American seismologists Harry Wood and Frank Neumann, the scale (now called the modified Mercalli scale) rates the intensity of earthquakes from levels I (detected only by seismographic instruments) through XII (destruction of all buildings).

On the modified Mercalli scale, a rating of II or III describes a weak earthquake that is felt by few people. At this strength, ground vibrations are similar to the passing of a large truck. People on upper floors of buildings would most likely feel such small tremors as a slight swaying motion. Tremors of this strength may also cause hanging objects like chandeliers to swing.

Medium-strength earthquakes with a modified Mercalli rating from IV to VI are felt by most people and usually wake those who are asleep. Earthquakes of this intensity can cause walls to crack and dishes and windows to move or break. During this type of earthquake, unstable objects may fall over or drop to the floor, heavy furniture may move across the floor, and people may feel off-balance as they walk.

Earthquakes with a VII or VIII rating on the modified Mercalli scale can cause considerable damage to poorly designed and built structures. Even well-built structures may suffer moderate damage. An earthquake of this strength can cause chimneys, factory stacks, columns, and walls to tumble, and unsecured houses to move off their foundations. The ground motion may cause wet ground to develop cracks and sand and mud to spurt up through those cracks.

Serious damage and partial-to-total collapse of buildings—even specially designed structures—is common in earthquakes rating IX or higher on the modified Mercalli scale. Underground water pipes, reservoirs, dams, and embankments break or become damaged. Railroad rails may bend, and noticeable cracks may appear in the ground. Liquefaction occurs, causing buildings and roads to sink into the ground. Landslides occur on steep slopes. At level XII of the scale, the ground ripples in waves, objects are thrown into the air, and the courses of rivers may shift.

Richter scale In 1935 American seismologist Charles Richter (1900–1985) developed a scale to measure the magnitude of earthquakes. Richter and colleague Beno Gutenberg (1889–1960) sought a standard method of measuring and comparing earthquakes. Up to that point, the Mercalli scale was the only earthquake-measurement tool. The problem

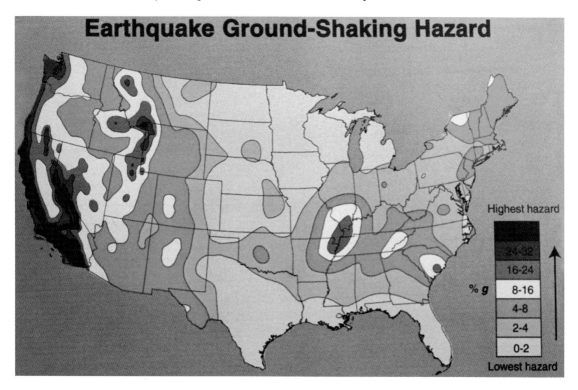

Earthquake hazard map. AP IMAGES.

Charles F. Richter, creator of the Richter scale, studying data from earthquake detection equipment in California in 1963. AP IMAGES.

with the Mercalli scale, however, was that it depended on nonscientific factors. It was greatly influenced by the soundness of building construction and the behaviors of the people living in the earthquake area. The Mercalli scale also made it difficult to rate earthquakes that occurred in rural areas where there were few buildings or people.

Richter and Gutenberg developed a way of measuring an earthquake's power, rather than its effects on humans or buildings. The Richter scale, ranging from 1 to 10, uses seismographic readings to compare the energy released by a specific earthquake to the energy released by other earthquakes. Each whole number increase in value on the scale indicates a ten-fold increase in the energy released and a thirty-fold increase in ground motion. Therefore, an earthquake with a value of 6.0 on the Richter scale is ten times more powerful than an earthquake with a value of 5.0, and so on up and down the scale.

Most earthquakes that are reported measure between 3.0 and 8.0 on the Richter scale. Those that have a rating less than 3.0 are not usually felt. Earthquakes measuring between 3.0 and 6.0 cause minor to moderate damage. Strong earthquakes, causing destruction in areas with large populations, measure between 6.0 and 6.9 on the scale. Earthquakes measuring 7.0 to 7.9 are major. (California is struck by earthquakes in this range about once every eighteen years.) Any earthquake that measures 8.0 or above on the Richter scale is considered a massive earthquake, one that causes widespread destruction. An earthquake of this magnitude generally occurs somewhere on the planet once every five to ten years.

Earthquake prediction   Of the more than one million earthquakes that shake the surface of Earth each year, the vast majority measure 3.4 or below on the Richter scale and cannot be felt by people. The few earthquakes that register high on the Richter scale, however, can be disastrous. Great earthquakes have accounted for some of the most dreadful natural disasters in recorded human history. In the past eight hundred years, seventeen earthquakes have caused fifty thousand or more deaths apiece.

Earthquake rattles Washington State

At 10:54 AM on February 28, 2001, northwest Washington state was rocked by its most powerful earthquake in fifty-two years. The forty-second tremor measured 6.8 on the Richter scale. It was centered between Olympia and Tacoma, some 30 miles from Seattle, on the southern border of Puget Sound. The quake produced just one fatality (one woman died of a heart attack) and approximately 235 injuries; only a handful of the injuries were serious, and none were life-threatening.

Damage caused by the earthquake was estimated at more than two billion dollars. Examples of damage included crumbled bridges, buckled roads and sidewalks, and broken glass and fallen plaster in buildings. Some of the worst destruction occurred at the seventy-four-year-old capitol building in Olympia, about 12 miles from the earthquake's epicenter. The building's dome was cracked in several places, and engineers were unsure as to whether or when the statehouse could be used again.

Geologists noted that the damage in the region was relatively minor for a quake of that magnitude. They attributed the gentleness of the earthquake to the location of its epicenter, which was more than 30 miles beneath the surface. "We were very, very lucky," stated Washington governor Gary Lock in the New York Times of March 2, 2001. "There could have been utter catastrophe had it been higher, closer to the surface."

Also deserving credit for the prevention of greater damage was the strict earthquake code for building construction in the region. Those regulations are intended to protect buildings from all but catastrophic earthquakes. Almost all buildings built or upgraded to be in compliance with the code escaped without serious damage.

Seismologists in many countries constantly monitor the stresses within Earth's crust. Ultrasensitive instruments placed across faults at the surface measure the slow, almost imperceptible movement of plates. Other instruments measure phenomena that sometimes precede earthquakes, including changes in tide and groundwater levels, fluctuations in the magnetic properties of rocks, and the swelling or tilting of the ground.

For more than thirty-five years, the U.S. Geological Survey (USGS) has operated seismographic stations throughout the world. In the mid-1990s, the USGS and the Incorporated Research Institutions for Seismology (an association of more than ninety universities) developed the Global Seismographic Network (GSN). This worldwide network is composed of 128 stations in more than eighty countries on all continents. Its purpose is to make readily available high-quality data regarding earthquakes. Within minutes after data is received and recorded, scientists can analyze the information to determine the location and magnitude of any large seismic event that has occurred anywhere on the planet.

Earthquake braces installed at Diablo Canyon nuclear power plant in California. ©ROGER RESSMEYER/CORBIS.

Even with this state-of-the-art equipment, scientists cannot predict the exact time and place an earthquake will occur. Earthquake researchers continue to sharpen their ability to correctly interpret the significance of seismic activity. At present, scientists rely primarily on information about past earthquakes in order to determine the likelihood of future earthquakes.

Some people look to peculiar animal behaviors as a sign of impending earthquakes. Certain animals have heightened sensitivities to electricity, magnetic fields, odors, and vibrations. In China it is said that prior to earthquakes snails come out of the ground, rats leave houses, birds fly from their nests, and dogs bark constantly. In Japan, there are reports of goldfish swimming frantically just before earthquakes. From a scientific standpoint, however, the connection between animal behavior and earthquakes has not been proven.

A matter of survival: How can we live through earthquakes?

Earthquakes can neither be stopped nor controlled, but humans can minimize the destruction earthquakes cause. A seemingly simple solution is for people to avoid living in earthquake-prone areas. This solution is not very practical, however, since many cities—some with large and growing populations—already stand in these areas.

A more realistic solution is to design structures resistant to earthquake damage. In many earthquake zones, strict building codes for new structures have been adopted. For existing buildings, internal and external braces have been added to strengthen them. Buildings have also been anchored to their foundations to keep them from slipping off during an earthquake.

Builders in earthquake zones now use metal straps or braces to help strengthen a building's (especially a tall building's) resistance to earthquakes. They use materials and designs that can absorb or withstand ground vibrations. They also put layers of rubber and steel underneath new buildings to lessen the effect of an earthquake on the building itself.

Bridges can also be constructed to withstand earthquakes. San Francisco's Golden Gate Bridge, for instance, has a flexible structure that allows it to sway but not break during most earthquakes. Cantilever bridges (type of bridge made of two sections that extend outward from banks or piers and join together in the middle), like the San Francisco-Oakland Bay Bridge, in contrast, are less flexible and more prone to collapse during earthquakes.

Personal safety An earthquake is unpredictable and terrifying, but people caught in one can follow a few steps to help reduce personal injury. Safety experts recommend the following:

- First and foremost, do not panic. The shaking of the ground is not harmful; falling objects are.
- If you are indoors when an earthquake hits, stay there. Crawl beneath and hang onto a heavy desk or table. If that is not possible, move into a hallway or crouch against an inside wall. Stay away from windows, fireplaces, and heavy standing objects. Get out of the kitchen—stoves and heavy appliances make it a dangerous place. Do not run downstairs or rush outside while the house or building is shaking.
- If you are outside when an earthquake hits, move quickly into an open area away from buildings, power lines, walls, or other structures that might fall.
- If you are driving when an earthquake hits, move the car out of traffic as quickly and carefully as possible and stop. Do not park on or under a bridge or overpass, or under trees, light posts, power lines, signs, or anything else that might fall. Stay inside the car until the tremors stop.

- If in a mountainous area, move into a clearing or open area. Be mindful of landslides, falling rocks, or other loose debris that could come rolling down a slope.

After the tremors of an earthquake subside, remember to do the following:

- Check the utilities. If the smell of gas is present in the air, turn off the main gas valve and open the windows, if possible. Do not light matches or lighters. Do not turn on electrical equipment or appliances. A spark from any of these may cause an explosion and fire. Leave the house or building and report the gas leak.
- Use the telephone only to report an emergency. If there is an emergency and the telephone lines are down, send someone for help.
- Stay out of damaged buildings. Aftershocks (tremors that occur after the main shock of an earthquake) can topple already weakened structures.
- Advance preparation for an earthquake, like for any disaster, can greatly reduce the chances of injury or death. Develop an earthquake plan at home or at school that explains the safest course of action should an earthquake strike. Keep on hand an emergency kit that includes a flashlight, a battery-powered radio, extra batteries, first-aid materials, a fire extinguisher, canned or packaged food (with a manual can opener), plastic containers filled with drinking water (allow at least one gallon or three liters per person per day), warm clothes, matches, candles, and a camp stove or barbecue with extra fuel (stored carefully).

[*See Also* **Tsunami**]

For More Information

BOOKS

Bolt, Bruce A. *Earthquakes.* 3rd ed. Salt Lake City, UT: W. H. Freeman, 1993.

Bronson, William. *The Earth Shook, the Sky Burned.* San Francisco, CA: Chronicle Books, 1959; reprinted, 1997.

Keller, Edward A., and Nicholas Pinter. *Active Tectonics: Earthquakes, Uplift, and Landscape.* Upper Saddle River, NJ: Prentice Hall, 1996.

Newton, David E. *Earthquakes.* New York: Franklin Watts, 1993.

Ritchie, David. *The Encyclopedia of Earthquakes and Volcanoes.* New York: Facts on File, 1994.

PERIODICALS

"Assessing Quake's Damage." *New York Times* (March 2, 2001): p. A21.

El Niño

In the late 1990s, the weather news was dominated by a phenomenon called El Niño (pronounced el-NEE-nyo). El Niño is a disruption of the ocean-atmosphere system in the tropical Pacific characterized by elevated water temperatures off the coast of Peru. Water temperatures may rise by 5 to 11°F (3 to 6°C). During an El Niño event, the Pacific coast of South America may experience floods, while Australia may suffer drought conditions. The event may also trigger unusual weather disturbances all over the Western Hemisphere. While El Niño is not new—indeed, its occurrence has been recorded for centuries—only in the past few decades have scientists begun to understand the mechanics and scope of this climate-altering event.

The term "el niño" is Spanish for "the child." When it is capitalized as "El Niño," it means "the Christ child." The name was given by sailors in the late 1800s to a weak warm current that appeared off the coast of Ecuador and Peru each year around Christmastime. The term "El Niño" first appeared in print in a Peruvian scientific journal in 1892.

There is evidence that strong El Niños have occurred periodically for thousands of years. In the late 1990s an unusually strong El Niño was blamed for floods, droughts, wildfires, storms, and unseasonable temperatures around the world.

Defining El Niño

El Niño has traditionally been defined as the annual warming of the waters off the coast of Peru. A massive pool of warm water—containing twenty to thirty times as much water as all the Great Lakes combined—arrives from the western Pacific equatorial region, replacing the cold water that typically resides on the South American coast. Most years the warm water only persists for a month or so before the cold water returns.

The water off the coast of Peru is typically about 68°F (20°C). During El Niño years, the water warms—sometimes just slightly and other times

283

by several degrees. During El Niño conditions in December 1997, for example, the water temperature off the coast of Peru was 77°F (25°C).

A telltale sign that El Niño has arrived is the dwindling of fish populations (anchovies, in particular). Large numbers of fish die off or migrate to less-affected areas because the warm water is unable to sustain the tiny animals that fish eat. In scientific terms, the warm water is nutrient poor. The cold water, which is considered nutrient rich, does support tiny marine organisms. As the warm water moves in and these microorganisms die, it becomes nutrient poor.

In recent times the term "El Niño" has come to mean only extraordinarily strong El Niño episodes. Such episodes generally occur every three to seven years, but sometimes happen as often as every two years or as infrequently as every ten years. During these events, coastal waters become significantly warmer than usual—up to 10°F (5.6°C) higher than normal. In addition, the warm waters last longer than a few months (the longest recorded El Niño lasted four years, from 1991–1995) and occupy much of the eastern Pacific Ocean.

Commonly accepted standards for what constitutes a major El Niño event (that from hereon will simply be called an "El Niño") were developed by the Japanese Meteorological Agency (JMA). Those criteria, or conditions that must be met, are as follows: 1. Pacific Ocean temperatures, along the equator from Papua New Guinea in the west to the Galápagos Islands in the east, must be an average of 1°F (0.5°C) above normal; 2. The warm waters must persist for more than six months.

The 1997 to 1998 El Niño

In April 1997 the strongest El Niño in recorded history got underway. It produced heavy rain and flooding on the Pacific coast of South America, in California, along the U.S. Gulf Coast, in Eastern Europe, and in East Africa. Drought and wildfires spread in Australia, Southeast Asia, Mexico, Central America, Texas, Florida, and northeastern Brazil. A series of hurricanes swept through the eastern and western Pacific.

More acres of tropical rain forest burned during the El Niño of 1997–98 than at any other time in recorded history. By the time the episode ended in May 1998, the worldwide death toll due to El Niño—related weather was approximately 23,000, and property damage totaled at least thirty-three billion dollars.

WORDS TO KNOW

air pressure: the pressure exerted by the weight of air over a given area of Earth's surface. Also called atmospheric pressure or barometric pressure.

ecosystem: a community of plants and animals, including humans, and their physical surroundings.

El Niño: means "the Christ child" in Spanish. A period of unusual warming of the Pacific Ocean waters off the coast of Peru and Ecuador. It usually starts around Christmas, which is how it got its name.

ENSO: stands for El Niño/Southern Oscillation. It describes the simultaneous warming of the waters in the eastern Pacific Ocean and the shifting pattern of air pressure between the eastern and western edges of the Pacific.

food chain: transfer of food energy from one organism to another. It begins with a plant species, which is eaten by an animal species; it continues with a second animal species, which eats the first, and so on.

jet stream: the world's fastest upper-air winds. Jet streams travel in a west-to-east direction, at speeds of 80 to 190 miles (130 to 300 kilo-

meters) per hour, around 30,000 feet (9,150 meters) above the ground. Jet streams occur where the largest differences in air temperature and air pressure exist. In North America, jet streams are typically found over southern Canada and the northern United States, as well as over the southern United States and Mexico. The northern jet stream is called the polar jet stream, and the southern jet stream is called the subtropical jet stream.

La Niña: Spanish for "little girl," a period of unusual cooling of the Pacific Ocean waters off the coast of Peru and Ecuador. It often follows an El Niño.

monsoon: a name for seasonal winds that result in a rainy season occurring in the summer on tropical continents, when the land becomes warmer than the sea beside it.

numerical prediction model: a computer program that mathematically duplicates conditions in nature. It is often used to predict the weather.

trade winds: dominant surface winds near the equator, generally blowing from east to west and toward the equator.

upwelling: the rising up of cold waters from the depths of the ocean, replacing the warm surface water that has moved away horizontally.

Droughts and wildfires   Southeast Asia, plagued by drought (prolonged periods of unusually dry conditions) and wildfires, was the hardest hit area of the 1997–98 El Niño. Indonesia was hit with its worst drought in fifty years. Fires claimed more than twelve million acres of Indonesian and Malaysian rain forest in 1997, and 7.5 million acres in early 1998. (The fires predominantly burned on the islands of Sumatra and Borneo. Sumatra is part of Indonesia and Borneo is divided between the countries of Indonesia and Malaysia.) Relief, in the form of rain, came in May 1998.

The fires were set by farmers who burn the land to clear it for planting. Most years, any lingering flames are put out by the September monsoon. In 1997, however, the monsoon rains were delayed until December. The fires spread rapidly through the parched trees, propelled by hot winds. This method of clearing land for planting, called slash-and-burn agriculture, was outlawed after the 1997 fires. (The law, however, is proving hard to enforce, especially in remote regions).

The smoke from the fires was so thick that the Sun was blocked for days and drivers turned on their headlights at noon. Schools and businesses were shut down, and birds fell from the sky. People were advised to wear face masks outdoors in Indonesia, Malaysia, Singapore, the Philippines, and Thailand. Hundreds of people died of respiratory ailments, and tens of thousands were sickened.

In Sumatra, poor visibility in September 1997 was responsible for the crash of an airplane that killed 234 people. The smoke traveled thousands of miles to the west, affecting air quality and visibility on the Maldives, an island group in the Indian Ocean. Crop losses plagued much of the region. In Indonesia and Malaysia millions of people suffered shortages of food and drinking water. The fires carried a price tag of at least 1.3 billion dollars; the damages due to the haze alone tallied another one billion dollars.

Australia was hit by a severe drought in 1997. Cattle ranchers were forced, due to the lack of water and food, to slaughter their herds. In neighboring Papua New Guinea, drought resulted in widespread hunger. By the end of 1997 several hundred people had died as a result of famine and famine-related diseases, and half a million people were in urgent need of food and water.

In the spring of 1998, drought in the United States struck the Southwest and the Southeast. Texas's rainy winter of 1997–98 gave way to its third driest spring on record, in 1998. Accompanying Texas's drought was one of its worst heat waves of the century, claiming thirty lives.

In March, April, and May 1998, drought and wildfires came to Mexico, Central America, and northeast Brazil. Mexico lost more than 1.25 million wooded acres to fire. Smoke from those fires reduced visibility throughout much of Texas and spread haze and soot as far away as Wisconsin, Florida, and Oklahoma.

Due to drought conditions in the spring of 1998, the Rio Grande River in Texas fell to its lowest levels in years. AP IMAGES.

The source of Mexico's fires, like those of Southeast Asia, was a combination of slash-and-burn agriculture and exceedingly dry conditions. Fires also burned out of control in Guatemala, Honduras, El Salvador, Nicaragua, and Costa Rica, leading each of those countries to be declared disaster areas. The fires in Mexico and Central America were finally extinguished in May and June, when El Niño faded and the rains fell.

Floods Rain and snow fell heavily in South America in 1997 and 1998. Ten times the normal amount of rain for the period had fallen in central Chile by mid-August 1997. Floods and mud slides damaged crops, buildings, roads, and bridges. In Chile's Atacama Desert, one of the driest places in the world, heavy rains washed out roads. Rain that drenched the central Andes caused serious flooding in Chile's capital city, Santiago. Paraguay, Uruguay, northeastern Argentina, and southern Brazil also endured heavy rain and sustained damages to buildings and crops.

From November 1997 through May 1998, storms, floods, and mud slides in Peru and neighboring Ecuador claimed 450 lives and did more than three billion dollars in damage to crops, roads, and buildings. Along the coast of Peru storms washed away some 300,000 homes, downed power lines, and destroyed roads and bridges. Waterborne diseases such as cholera and hepatitis, and mosquito-borne diseases such as malaria and dengue fever spread rapidly in coastal Peru.

Peruvian president Alberto Fujimori (pointing, on raft) observes flood damage near Ica, Peru, in 1998. AP IMAGES.

The town of Chato Chico, Peru, was washed away completely. In the Peruvian coastal town of Mampuesto, where floodwaters caused erosion in a cemetery, caskets and skeletons floated down the streets. A similarly macabre event occurred in Peru's third-largest city, Trujillo, where flooding in a cemetery emptied 123 graves and washed the corpses through the town. In the Peruvian Andes severe snowstorms caused the deaths of 2,500 alpacas, a cold-adapted, llama-like species.

In Peru's coastal Sechura Desert, normally so dry that the ground is hard and cracked, floodwaters formed a lake 90 miles (145 kilometers) long, 20 miles (32 kilometers) wide, and 10 feet (3 meters) deep. To ease food shortages, government officials stocked the temporary lake with fish.

California had its seventh-wettest winter of the century. Between December 1997 and March 1998, the state received between two and four times its normal rainfall. The Sierra Nevada mountain range in eastern California had nearly 200 inches (500 centimeters) of snow; in some spots the snowpack in March measured 20 feet (6 meters).

An early December storm caused street flooding in southern California, dumping 6.81 inches (17.30 centimeters) of rain in a 24-hour period. In February 1998 a storm packing 90 mile-per-hour (145 kilometer-per-hour) wind gusts invaded southern and central California. It downed trees

Heavy rains in Southern California damaged the Ventura Pier during El Niño–driven storms in 1997 and 1998. AP IMAGES.

and power lines and produced flooding and mud slides. Waves up to 35 feet (10.7 meters) high pounded the coast. Just south of San Francisco, mud slides on the cliffs of Pacifica washed homes into the bay.

Also due to heavy rains in California, some two thousand cattle were stuck in knee-deep mud and died. The flooding also led to crop losses of strawberries, tomatoes, and lettuce. Agricultural losses were estimated at 200 million dollars.

Seventeen people lost their lives in storms and flooding during the California winter. Total El Niño–related property damages (including agricultural losses) throughout the state ran approximately one billion dollars.

The damage toll would have been far greater had Californians not been preparing for the onslaught of El Niño. Since early 1997, residents had been building dikes to keep back ocean water, clearing flood-control channels, and repairing roofs. In Redondo Beach, for example, high waves washed away the sand barriers built to protect the beach but left the beach intact.

East Africa, which usually suffers from drought during El Niños, was inundated with rain. The rain, which fell from October 1997 through January 1998, drowned crops and led to famine throughout the region. Relief agencies set up soup kitchens in Sudan, Somalia, and Kenya, all hard hit by flooding. In Somalia floods claimed the lives of more than 2,300

Sudanese women sit outside their homes in Khartoum following heavy rains in 1999. AP IMAGES.

people, left 250,000 people homeless, and submerged entire villages. Some 100 people were killed in Kenya due to flooding in January 1998.

People and farm animals in Kenya and Somalia also suffered from mosquito-borne diseases that spread as a result of El Niño's rains. Many farmers lost up to 90 percent of their camels, cows, sheep, and goats to an illness, characterized by severe bleeding, called Rift Valley fever. There was also an outbreak of Rift Valley fever among humans—some eighty-nine thousand people were infected. Although the illness is not usually fatal to humans, it exacted a death toll of two hundred people that season.

A strengthened jet stream (the world's fastest upper-air winds) brought abundant rainfall to much of Europe in May and June of 1997. Southwestern Poland, the Czech Republic, eastern Germany, northeastern Hungary, Romania, and northern Slovakia experienced some of their worst floods of the century. Floods claimed the lives of fifty-five people in Poland and sixty people in the Czech Republic. There was more than two billion dollars in damage in the region. Some 300,000 cattle were lost in the Czech Republic and around one million chickens died when Polish farms were flooded.

Hurricanes and typhoons As predicted for an El Niño year, Atlantic hurricane activity in 1997 was greatly reduced (the hurricane season for the Northern Hemisphere runs from June through December). The only Atlantic hurricane to make landfall in the United States was Hurricane Danny. Danny struck the Gulf Coast in July, bringing high winds and flooding to Louisiana and Alabama. Danny caused four deaths and 100 million dollars in damage.

In contrast, in 1997 there were seven major hurricanes in the Pacific Ocean (those that occur in the western North Pacific are called typhoons). A major hurricane is defined as one that is at least a Category 3 on the Saffir-Simpson scale of hurricane intensity. A category 3 storm does extensive damage and has winds between 111 and 130 miles per hour (179 and 209 kilometers per hour). In an average year the Pacific spawns five major hurricanes.

Hurricane Linda, which lashed Mexico's west coast in mid-September 1997, packed 185 mile-per-hour (298 kilometer-per-hour) winds. By way of comparison, Hurricane Andrew, which did extensive damage to Florida in 1992, had winds of 130 miles (209 kilometers) per hour. Linda—one of the strongest hurricanes ever recorded in the eastern Pacific—was so severe that meteorologists proposed adding a new category, Category 6, to the Saffir-Simpson Scale (the scale presently goes up to 5).

In late September 1997, Hurricane Nora made landfall on Mexico's Baja California peninsula. It then headed north, bringing heavy rains and flooding to Los Angeles and Arizona. Three people were killed in traffic accidents in Los Angeles and San Diego during the storm, and 1,000 people had to evacuate their homes in Arizona.

The following month Mexico's west coast was devastated by Hurricane Pauline. Heavy rains, floods, and mud slides killed as many as 230 people in Acapulco and surrounding areas, and destroyed thousands of homes. Tourists and residents faced shortages of food and drinking water for several days before rescue crews could reach them.

Weather report: El Niño is hardest on the poor

Around the world, poor people bear the brunt of El Niño. One reason for this reality is that it is more difficult for poor people to escape affected areas. Poor people are therefore more likely to suffer, and die, from drought-related famine or flooding-related illness. Poor people often live in flimsy or substandard housing that is vulnerable to floods; slums sustain the greatest damage due to mud slides and coastal flooding. For people who have little or no financial safety net, a loss of one's home or farm means financial ruin. Another factor is that governments often tend first to the needs of their most powerful constituencies—wealthy and middle-class people—while the needs of the poor are overlooked.

During the 1998 El Niño, when northeast Brazil suffered from drought and famine, poor people in that nation fought back against a neglectful government. Hungry crowds, angered at the failure of the government to distribute relief supplies, looted supermarkets and food trucks. Many of the nation's Catholic priests supported the rebellion, claiming that looting is justified when survival is at stake.

Weather report: United States has typical El Niño winter in 1997–98

In general, the winter of 1997–98 in the United States was typical of an El Niño winter. The polar jet stream, which runs over central Canada, ran farther north than usual, through central Canada, keeping cold, polar air out of the northern United States and southern Canada. From Bismarck, North Dakota, to Buffalo, New York, temperatures were between 5 and 10°F (3 and 6°C) higher than normal. One way to gauge the severity of a winter is by looking at heating bills; northerners spent approximately 10 percent less on fuel in the winter of 1997–98 than they do on average.

Also as predicted, a strengthened subtropical jet stream brought increased precipitation and below-normal temperatures to the southern United States. Several southern cities, such as Tampa, Florida; New Orleans, Louisiana; and Charleston, South Carolina, had record rainfall during the winter of 1997–98. The state of Florida recorded its wettest winter ever. The Deep South experienced a rare snowstorm in December 1997. Four-to-eight inches of snow blanketed central Mississippi and central Alabama. Heavy snow also fell on the Southwest and the southern Plains states that month.

Typhoon Winnie whirled across the western Pacific in August 1997, striking the Philippines, Taiwan, and China. Winnie claimed nearly three hundred lives. In early November Typhoon Linda struck the southern tip of Vietnam. Nearly 100,000 homes were lost to the storm's winds and rains. Some three thousand people, most of them fishermen, died in the storm and flooding.

In December 1997, a strong hurricane formed over the El Niño–warmed waters south of Hawaii. Hurricanes rarely form in this region. Typhoon Paka, as it was named, soaked Guam in the southern Mariana Islands on December 16. Winds were measured at 108 miles per hour (174 kilometers per hour) before they destroyed instruments at a weather station on Guam.

Ice storms, tornadoes, and other unusual events   In January 1998 southeastern Canada and New England experienced the region's worst ice storm in recent history. (Meteorologists are divided as to whether or not El Niño is to blame for this event.) Freezing rain fell for five days, bringing down trees, power lines, and high-voltage towers in Eastern Ontario, New Brunswick, Nova Scotia, Maine, Vermont, New Hampshire, and upstate New York. At least twenty-five people lost their lives to the storm. Power was lost for more than four million people—including more than half the population of Maine—most of them for over a week. There was more than one billion dollars in damage to homes, businesses, and power systems throughout the region. More than 18 million acres of forestland were damaged in Maine, New Hampshire, Vermont, and upstate New York. The damage cost was estimated at between 650 million and 1.4 billion dollars.

During the unusually warm spring, which was blamed on El Niño, the ice melted and caused flooding through much of central Canada. Around 5,000 people were forced to evacuate their homes as channels overflowed their banks, turning streets into rivers, in Quebec and Ontario provinces.

A pedestrian walks around downed branches and power lines following a severe ice storm in Watertown, New York, in 1998. AP IMAGES.

The southeastern United States experienced a spate of deadly tornadoes in the spring of 1998. On the night of February 22, forty-one people were killed, many as they slept, as tornadoes tore through central Florida. The tornadoes destroyed more than 800 homes and damaged more than 3,500 more, at a cost of more than 500 million dollars. A tornado that struck northeast Georgia on March 20 took twelve lives. On April 8 and 9, a string of tornadoes in Georgia and Alabama left thirty-four people dead and some five thousand acres of forests destroyed.

Dangerous science: What causes an El Niño?

While scientists have made great strides in recent years toward understanding and predicting El Niño, the origins of El Niño remain a mystery. At present, there are three primary theories as to what triggers an El Niño event: undersea volcanic eruptions, sunspots (magnetic storms on the Sun's surface), and the previous El Niño.

The first theory rests on the assumption that eruptions and lava leaks from volcanoes that dot the floor of the eastern Pacific Ocean provide enough heat to put an El Niño in motion. This theory is supported by the large number of earthquakes that have occurred on the ocean floor, west of South America, during recent El Niños. There is a strong link between the occurrence of undersea earthquakes and volcanic eruptions.

The second theory suggests that the ocean warming at the start of an El Niño is connected to the cycle of sunspots. Sunspots are areas of magnetic disturbance on the surface of the Sun, sometimes referred to as storms. When these storms reach maturity they eject plasma—an extremely hot substance made of charged particles—into space. A link has been established between increased sunspot activity and warmer temperatures on Earth. Scientists are attempting to determine whether the amount of warming during increased sunspot activity is sufficient to trigger an El Niño.

The third theory is that El Niños occur in cycles, with each successive El Niño being set in motion by the one before it. The theory goes like this: as an El Niño weakens, it generates long ocean waves, called Rossby waves, that travel westward across the Pacific. The Rossby waves carry with them the warm surface waters. As the warm layer thins in the eastern Pacific, cold water upwells to take its place.

The mass of warm water, driven by westward-blowing trade winds, then piles up in the western Pacific. When the pile of water in the west becomes so steep (up to five feet above mean sea level) that the trade winds can stack it no higher, the water is drawn down by gravity and flows back to the east. The shifting position of the warm waters creates a change in the air pressure gradient, and the trade winds weaken or reverse direction. The next El Niño is underway.

The influence of oceans on global weather As scientists have recently discovered, El Niño is second only to the changing seasons as the strongest factor influencing world weather patterns. The reason for El Niño's strength has to do with the role of oceans in regulating weather, and with the enormous amount of energy contained in El Niño's warm waters.

Oceans cover more than 70 percent of the Earth's surface and are responsible for about one-third of total heat distribution around the planet. It is estimated that the top ten feet (three meters) of the ocean water contains as much heat as the total atmosphere.

The heat that is stored in oceans rises into the air above. The warm, moist air ascends and forms clouds. The water vapor within the clouds condenses and falls to the ground as rain. Therefore, it stands to reason that the world's wettest zones are the regions in which ocean temperatures are highest.

The central Pacific Ocean (near the equator), the world's longest continuous open body of water, is a tremendous storehouse of solar energy. Most of the time, the warmest water is concentrated in a deep layer in the western central Pacific, near eastern Australia and Indonesia. Accordingly, that region has a rainy climate. The waters in the eastern Pacific, off the coast of Peru and Ecuador, are much cooler. With less heat to rise into the air, comparatively little rain falls in that region.

During El Niño, the pool of warm water moves eastward across the Central Pacific. The South American coast receives the heavy rains that typically fall in the western Pacific.

The thermocline   Meteorologists (scientists who study weather and climate) explain El Niño as a shift in the thermocline. The thermocline is an imaginary dividing line between warm surface water and the cooler water below in the ocean. Under normal conditions, the thermocline is around 500 feet (150 meters) below the surface in the western Pacific and around 165 feet (50 meters) below the surface in the eastern Pacific. In other words, the warm water extends to a depth of 500 feet in the west and 165 feet in the east. Directly off the coast of Peru, cold water churns up from below and cools the surface water—bringing the thermocline nearly to the surface.

Under El Niño conditions, when the warm surface water heads eastward, the thermocline nearly levels out (it remains slightly lower in the western Pacific than in the eastern Pacific). The layer of warm water off the Peruvian coast is so deep that even water churned up from below is warm.

The trade winds connection   In the early 1960s Norwegian-born American meteorologist Jacob Bjerknes (1897–1975) discovered a link between the warming of waters in the eastern Pacific Ocean and a shift in the direction of the major surface winds at the equator, called the trade winds. Trade winds are a class of global winds—winds that bring warm air to cold areas and cold air to warm areas around the planet. Global winds rise and fall and move along the Earth's surface through a series of loops, or cells, on their route from the equator to the poles and back.

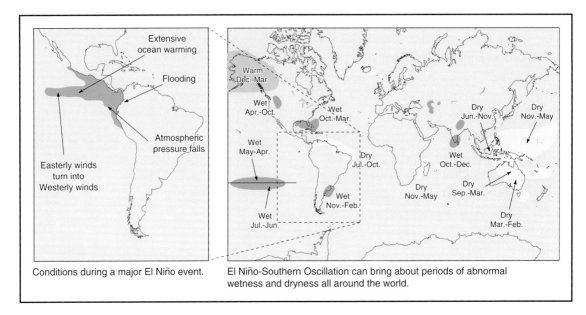

Conditions during a major El Niño event.

El Niño-Southern Oscillation can bring about periods of abnormal wetness and dryness all around the world.

El Niño and the Southern Oscillation.

Trade winds originate in the Northern Hemisphere at approximately 30° north (this runs through the southern tip of Florida) and in the Southern Hemisphere at approximately 30° south (this runs through the Amazonian region of South America). At those latitudes air sinks to the surface, warming as it descends, and blows toward the equator. In the Northern Hemisphere trade winds blow to the southwest, and in the Southern Hemisphere trade winds blow to the northwest.

Every so often the trade winds weaken or reverse direction (begin blowing toward the east) in the tropical Pacific Ocean. That change is called the Southern Oscillation (oscillation means shift, swing, or variation). The Southern Oscillation is brought about by a shifting pattern of air pressure between the eastern and western edges of the Pacific Ocean. Air pressure, also known as barometric pressure or atmospheric pressure, is the weight of the air over a given area. Wind flows from areas of high air pressure to areas of low air pressure, in an attempt to equalize conditions.

As it turns out, El Niño and the Southern Oscillation occur at the same time. Years marked by El Niño and the Southern Oscillation are called El Niño/Southern Oscillation, or ENSO, years (they are sometimes called warm-phase ENSO years).

Air pressure and water temperature in normal years and ENSO years   During normal years (also called cold-phase ENSO years) air pressure is higher over the eastern Pacific, near South America, and lower over the western Pacific, near Australia. (High pressure is typically associated with clear skies while low pressure is typically associated with cloudy skies and rain.) This pressure gradient (change in air pressure across a horizontal distance) drives the trade winds from east to west, and toward the equator. The winds carry warmth and moisture toward Australia and Indonesia.

At the same time, the winds push along the surface layer of warm water, actually increasing the sea level in the western Pacific. In contrast, the sea level along the coast of tropical South America lowers, and the top layer of warm water thins. Cold water from the depths of the ocean along the South American shores rises to the surface and replaces the warm water. The water in the western Pacific is typically 14°F (8°C) warmer than the water in the eastern Pacific.

Just prior to an ENSO year, the easterly (coming from the east) trade winds weaken and sometimes reverse direction, and the warm waters in the western Pacific begin to move eastward. The warm water flows eastward in a long chain of waves called Kelvin waves. The air pressure in the eastern Pacific decreases, while the air pressure in the western Pacific rises.

The warm water, stretching for a distance of thousands of miles, piles up on the coasts of Peru and Ecuador. The layer of warm water becomes so deep along the South American coast that upwelling, or rising cold water, only brings up warm water (the cold water that normally rises to the surface on the South American coast is too far submerged). As the warm water evaporates into the air and forms clouds, the coastal South American nations experience an excess of rain, which causes flooding and

Experiment: Measuring atmospheric pressure

Changes in air pressure over the Pacific Ocean help bring about the weakened and reversed trade winds that are a hallmark of the ENSO. Scientists use an instrument called a barometer to measure air pressure. To understand how barometers work, try this experiment.

Get a balloon and a clean glass jar with a wide top (such as a mayonnaise jar or a peanut butter jar). Use scissors to cut off the neck of the balloon. Brush some rubber cement or glue around the rim of the jar, and the stretch the balloon over the jar so that you have a nearly flat piece of rubber stretched over and glued to the mouth of the jar. Tape a straw to the top of the balloon so that one end of the straw is in the middle of the mouth of the jar and the straw sits parallel to the floor.

When air pressure goes down, the air in the jar will expand, causing the balloon to swell and the straw to point down. When the air pressure goes up, outside air will expand into the jar. The balloon will get pushed down, and the straw will point up.

Who's who: Jacob Bjerknes and ENSO

Jacob Bjerknes (1897–1975), a Norwegian-born meteorologist teaching at the University of California, Los Angeles, put together the pieces of Sir Gilbert Walker's puzzle in 1969. Bjerknes had earlier gained fame as a meteorologist in Norway by describing the life cycle of storms in the middle latitudes (the regions of the world that lie between the latitudes of 30 degrees north and south, such as the United States and Europe).

Bjerknes became interested in the tropical Pacific during the strong El Niño of 1957–58. That event coincided with the International Geophysical Year (IGY), a year in which scientists the world over cooperated in a study of the earth (with an emphasis on oceans) and space.

As an IGY participant Bjerknes discovered that trade winds, or dominant surface winds near the equator, in the tropical Pacific Ocean weakened at the same time that waters warmed in the eastern Pacific. Soon thereafter he established a link between the arrival of warm waters and the following: heavy rains in South America; drought in the western Pacific; and the air pressure seesaw across the tropical Pacific (the Southern Oscillation). By 1969 Bjerknes had demonstrated conclusively that all these ocean-atmosphere interactions were intricately connected in a single, large-scale phenomenon that he called the El Niño/Southern Oscillation (ENSO).

erosion (removal of soil) while Australia, Indonesia, and the Philippines have unusually dry weather, and sometimes brush fires.

During a strong ENSO, the warm water doesn't stop once it reaches the shores of South America. Instead, it flows northward along the west coast of North America, sometimes as far north as northern Canada and Alaska. The moisture and heat rise from the ocean to the atmosphere, fueling storms that sweep eastward across North America.

Aftermath: The effects of El Niño

With the exception of the changing seasons, El Niño is the single greatest influence upon world weather patterns. El Niño's importance can be understood in terms of the role of oceans in controlling weather and the enormous amount of energy contained in El Niño's warm waters.

Oceans cover more than 70 percent of Earth's surface and are responsible for about one-third of total heat distribution around the planet. It is estimated that the top 10 feet (3 meters) of the ocean water contains as much heat as the entire atmosphere.

The heat that is stored in oceans warms the air just above the ocean's surface. This warm, moist air rises and is blown over land to form clouds. The water vapor within the clouds condenses into droplets and falls to the ground as rain. Because of this process, the world's wettest zones are the regions in which ocean temperatures are highest.

The central Pacific Ocean near the equator, the longest open body of water on Earth, is a tremendous storehouse of heat from the Sun. Most of the time, the warmest water is found in a deep

Who's who: Sir Gilbert Walker and the Southern Oscillation

In the 1920s British mathematician and physicist Sir Gilbert Walker (1868–1958) was the first to point out the connection between unusual weather events around the globe during certain years—now called El Niño years.

Walker began his research in 1903, when he was named head of the Indian Meteorological Service. Walker was charged with predicting when India's annual monsoon rains would fail (drought was a huge, reoccurring problem in India as it led to periodic famine and the starvation of large numbers of people). At that time, weather authorities believed that local factors, such as increased logging in the region's forests, were responsible for monsoon failures.

Walker sifted through local and global weather records, searching for clues that might explain a pattern of monsoon failures. After two decades of research, Walker made an important discovery. He found that in years when Asian monsoons failed, Australia and parts of Africa also experienced droughts.

Walker looked at air pressure readings for Australia (in the western Pacific) and Tahiti (in the eastern Pacific) for a period of several years. He discovered that in years when the monsoon failed, there was a shift in the pressure gradient (change in air pressure across a horizontal distance) across the ocean. Specifically he found that during dry years, pressure in the west was higher than usual and pressure in the east was lower than usual. Walker called this seesaw of the pressure gradient the Southern Oscillation.

Taking things one step further, Walker found a link between increased ocean temperatures and greater precipitation in the eastern Pacific. In reports written in the 1920s and 1930s, Walker provided evidence linking abnormal weather patterns around the world with the Southern Oscillation. He hypothesized that global weather patterns were set in motion by a combination of the Southern Oscillation and a warming of water in the eastern Pacific, but was unable to verify it. The missing ingredient in his equation was data on wind speed and direction across the Pacific. Walker's theory was proven correct in the 1960s, when Jacob Bjerknes collected the necessary information and put the pieces together.

While Walker made important strides toward understanding a global weather phenomenon, he failed in his task to predict monsoon failures in India. Even with today's sophisticated forecasting equipment, scientists are still grappling with that challenge.

layer in the western central Pacific, near Australia and Indonesia. Accordingly, that region has a rainy climate. The waters in the eastern Pacific, off the coast of Peru and Ecuador, are cooler. They put significantly less heat into the air; as a result, comparatively little rain falls in that region.

During El Niño, the pool of warm water moves eastward across the Central Pacific. The result is that the South American coast receives the heavy rains that usually fall in the western Pacific.

Weather report: Shifting air pressure patterns in the North Atlantic

In recent years more attention has been paid to the El Niño/Southern Oscillation's (ENSO) less-famous cousin, the North Atlantic Oscillation (NAO). The NAO is a balancing act between air pressure on the northern and southern reaches of the North Atlantic Ocean. Most years, the prevailing winds (winds blowing in the direction that's observed most often during a given time period) blow from a high-pressure region near the Azores (islands west of Portugal) northward to a low-pressure region near Iceland. From time to time, however, the pressure near Iceland declines. In the early years of the twenty-first century the pressure gradient appears to be weakening, which may indicate warmer summers and colder winters in Europe. However, long-term changes in the NAO indices are hard to predict and the winds weaken—this phenomenon is called an NAO event.

A normal pressure gradient has prevailed since the mid 1970s. The winter weather associated with this pattern is that Europe stays relatively warm while Canada stays relatively cold. When there is an NAO event, however, winter conditions cool down in Europe and warm up in Canada.

Through extensive research into the ENSO phenomena, scientists have determined that ENSO occurs every three to seven years. Understanding of NAO, in contrast, is still in its infancy and the phenomenon's period has yet to be discerned.

Effects of El Niño on the United States and Canada In the United States and Canada, El Niño is one factor among many that determines the weather. The effects of any given El Niño depend on the strength of the event, particularly the way in which it affects the positions of the jet streams.

El Niño's influence on the weather is always greatest in the winter. Winter is when El Niño reaches its most mature stage in the Northern Hemisphere. Winter is also when contrasts in temperatures between the north and south of North America are greatest, and when the jet streams are strongest. The following is a list of general weather trends observed during strong and weak El Niño episodes.

During a strong El Niño, the subtropical jet stream (over Mexico and the southern United States) strengthens over the southern United States, and sometimes merges with the polar jet stream. The strong subtropical jet stream can be seen on satellite photos as a band of clouds and moisture moving across Mexico and the southern United States. The jet stream brings greater-than-normal rainfall—and in some cases flash floods, mud slides, and tornadoes—to southern California, the southwestern United States, northern Mexico, and the Gulf Coast.

The jet stream sometimes dips south once it passes the Gulf Coast. If that happens the southeastern U.S. stays dry, sometimes giving way to wildfires, and has colder-than-usual winters.

If the subtropical and polar jet streams merge, the polar jet stream hovers farther south than usual. The polar jet stream acts as a barrier against cold polar air, keeping it to the north. When the jet stream shifts southward, it allows cold air to move farther south than usual. As a result, southern Canada and much of the northern United States experience cold and sometimes wet weather.

If the jet streams don't merge, the polar jet stream heads north to Alaska before heading eastward across central Canada. In that case southern Canada and the northern United States stay relatively warm and dry.

During a mild El Niño, a weaker subtropical jet stream crosses Mexico before swinging north over the southeastern United States. In that case the West Coast and Gulf states stay relatively dry—and often experience wildfires—while the Southeast gets rain and tornadoes.

The polar jet stream during a mild El Niño heads north into Canada on the western edge of the continent, then dips farther south than usual. With this arrangement the Pacific Northwest experiences dry weather, while the states in the Midwest and Northeast, as well as southern Canada, have cold, wet weather, and sometimes flooding.

The warm waters of El Niño also fuel the development of hurricanes in the equatorial eastern Pacific. Occasionally those hurricanes travel north and drench the coast of southern California, then travel eastward to Texas.

Effects of El Niño on Latin America and the Caribbean   El Niño's effect is experienced most directly on the west coast of South America, particularly in Peru and Ecuador. There the warming of the water disrupts the fishing-based economy. Under normal conditions, cold water, rich in nutrients, rises up from the depths of the ocean to the surface along the shore. The cold water contains phosphates and nitrates that sustain tiny marine plants called phytoplankton (pronounced FIE-toe-plank-ton). The phytoplankton are eaten by tiny marine animals called zooplankton. The zooplankton, in turn, are food for fish. Under El Niño conditions, warm water replaces the cold water. The warm water holds few nutrients; it is inhospitable to phytoplankton and, as a result, to zooplankton and fish. When the coastal water is warm, large numbers of fish die off or migrate in search of food.

While El Niño spells misfortune for fishermen in Peru and Ecuador, it is a blessing to coastal farmers. The warm water fuels intense storms that irrigate thirsty crops. To those farmers, El Niño years are known as *años de abundancia*—years of abundance. In some years, however, El Niño brings so much rain that flash floods occur, washing away homes and destroying fields.

Farther south, through the western and central portion of the continent—in Chile, Paraguay, and Argentina—El Niño brings excess moisture to normally arid (dry) regions. That precipitation falls in the form of

Exploring: El Niño and the anchovy industry

In the 1950s Peruvian fishermen expanded their anchovy harvesting operations. They sought to exploit markets in the United States and other industrialized nations for fishmeal—ground-up anchovies that are fed to poultry. In 1971 the Peruvian fishing fleet pulled nearly 14.1 million tons (13 million metric tons) of anchovies out of coastal waters, making Peru the world's top fishing nation.

The following year El Niño struck. As warm waters traveled to coastal Peru in 1972 and stayed throughout 1973, the anchovy population was greatly reduced. While the economic effects were felt most strongly by Peruvians, the lack of fishmeal also affected the U.S. poultry industry and other markets around the world. The number of anchovies still has not returned to pre-1972 levels.

rain in the lowlands and snow in the mountains. Water runs down from the mountains and floods low-lying cities. In Chile's Atacama Desert, one of the driest places in the world (it sometimes goes twenty years without a drop of rain), El Niño can bring enough rain to make wildflowers bloom and wash out roads. El Niño also brings heavier-than-usual rainfall to Uruguay and southern Brazil.

During an El Niño, the northeastern portion of Brazil, as well as Central America, the Caribbean, and southern Mexico usually suffer drought. During some El Niños, crop yields in the region are reduced, and the local populace goes hungry. The dry weather also increases the likelihood of forest fires.

The west coast of Mexico, in contrast to the inland portion of the country, experiences storms and Pacific hurricanes fueled by El Niño's warm waters.

Effects of El Niño on Africa, Asia, Australia, and Europe El Niño brings dry conditions—and often droughts and wildfires—to Australia, Southeast Asia, India, and Africa. In recent years, the worst El Niño–induced droughts occurred in Australia, India, Papua New Guinea, southeast Asia, and southern Africa. Wildfires raged out of control in Australia, Indonesia, and Malaysia. El Niño is unpredictable in eastern Africa; it sometimes brings drought and other times flooding. Central and eastern Europe sometimes experience excessively rainy weather during El Niño.

El Niño also spurs on the development of hurricanes in the Pacific Ocean (or cyclones, as they are called in the western Pacific region) and typhoons (another regional word for hurricane) in the Indian Ocean. During El Niño years, hurricanes and tropical storms (storm systems that form in the tropics and are weaker than hurricanes) dump heavy rains throughout much of Asia.

Effects of El Niño on animal life El Niño not only disrupts weather patterns, but it spells disaster for many types of marine life and land animals. As previously explained, the warm waters of El Niño are inhospitable to plankton, which occupy the bottom rung of the food chain. Fish, which feed on plankton, either move to colder waters or starve. (In a normal year there are six to eight million tons of anchovies in Peru's waters, but in an El Niño year there are only three to four million tons).

The repercussions of the lack of fish are felt all the way up the food chain and persist for several years. Marine birds and marine mammals (such as sea lions) that feed on fish throughout the Pacific Ocean face starvation. Populations of animals that prey upon sea birds also decline. The damage to marine life is observed throughout the Pacific region.

The spread of nutrient-poor, warm water is not the only way that El Niño affects animals. Other effects of El Niño imperil animal life in the following ways: river flooding results in the introduction of sediments and contaminants into coastal waters; large ocean waves erode wildlife habitat; and forest fires in drought-plagued regions drive wildlife out of their homes.

A key reference to: How El Niño reaches Africa and India

In 1982–83 southern Africa experienced severe drought, and India's monsoon rains, which usually occur during the summer, never came. While the lack of moisture in both places was blamed on El Niño, scientists have only recently determined the way in which El Niño influences regions beyond the Pacific.

It turns out that at the same time that waters warm off the coast of Peru, a similar warming occurs in the Indian Ocean. That warming triggers a reversal of the pressure gradient (the rate at which air pressure changes with horizontal distance) in the Indian Ocean. The surface winds that typically blow to the northwest, toward the coast of Africa and India, change direction. They blow toward the southeast, bringing warmth and moisture to western Australia and leaving southern Africa and India high and dry.

Sea birds   The animals most directly affected by the lack of fish are sea birds, primarily terns and gulls. In El Niño years sea birds in the western Pacific have difficulty finding enough food for themselves and their chicks. One of the biggest die-offs occurred during the 1957–58 El Niño, when some 18 million birds off the coast of Peru perished. Among the hardest-hit species were cormorants, boobies, and pelicans. Twenty-five years later, the 1982–83 El Niño drove away or killed 85 percent of Peru's sea birds. The seventeen million sea birds inhabiting Christmas Island (in the middle of the Pacific) also abandoned their homes at that time.

The 1997–98 El Niño also had a noticeable effect on sea birds. Albatrosses abandoned their nests in the Galápagos Islands in search of colder waters and more abundant fish. Peru's populations of Inca tern, guanay, and red-legged cormorant also suffered declines.

Weather report: El Niño weather around the world

Below is a summary of El Niño–inspired weather patterns around the world. This information presents general trends, not hard-and-fast rules. Weather during El Niño years is influenced by the strength of the event and a host of other factors. The weather in a given location during a particular El Niño may even be the opposite of what is listed below.

- **Increased precipitation and flooding:** Peru, Ecuador, Chile, Paraguay, Argentina, Uruguay, southern Brazil, east-central Africa, central and eastern Europe, western Australia, and eastward from California and Arizona through the southern United States.
- **Drought:** Northeastern Brazil, Central America, the Caribbean, and southern Mexico, Australia (except the west coast), India, southeast Asia, Papua New Guinea, California (during weak El Niño) and southern Africa.
- **Increased hurricane activity:** West coast of Mexico, southern California to Texas, Asia (along the coast of Indian Ocean), and Madagascar.
- **Warmer than usual winter:** Northern United States, western Canada, Alaska, northern Europe, southeast Asia, Japan, North Korea, South Korea, Mongolia, southeast Australia, and southeast Africa.
- **Colder than usual winter:** Southeastern United States.

The brown pelican population in Baja California and the Gulf of California (on Mexico's west coast) dropped to its lowest level in thirty years during the 1997–98 El Niño. In normal years there are between 10,000 and 20,000 nests in the colony. In March and April 1998, researchers found only 280 nests. Just one month later, not a single nest could be found. Biologists expected the pelicans to make a full recovery once the waters cooled and the anchovies, herrings, and sardines returned.

The decline of least terns in California during the El Niño of 1982–83 provides an interesting case study. The fish that terns typically feed on were few in number and small in size. Female terns laid their eggs later than usual, and the eggs were abnormally small. Many females abandoned their nests for lack of food, and many of the chicks that did hatch did not develop properly. Large numbers of the weakened chicks were preyed upon by small hawks called American kestrels.

The California least tern colony did not recover until 1988. The repercussions of the 1982–83 El Niño lasted so long, in part, because least terns do not breed until they are two or three years old. Thus, in 1984 and 1985 the number of breeding terns was smaller than usual.

Sea mammals Populations of sea lions, fur seals, and other sea mammals also decline during El Niño years. Those animals, which live in colonies on the South American coast, on the California coast, and on the Galápagos Islands (west of Ecuador), subsist mainly on anchovies. The scarcity of anchovies (and secondary food sources such as halibut, lantern fish, rockfish, and squid) during El Niño years has the most serious impact on young animals. Seal and sea lion pups go hungry because their mothers spend much more time than usual (five to six days, instead of the usual one to two days) seeking fish rather than nursing their young. Pups either starve or grow weak. Many of those pups that survive their first season later prove incapable of finding their own food, and die.

Large numbers of adult sea mammals also starve during El Niño years. Many females are unable to sustain themselves, particularly while nursing. Males are adversely affected by their breeding behaviors. They stay on land defending their territory during breeding season, typically going without food for several weeks. Once the males return to sea, they are unable to find sufficient food to regain their strength and survive.

During the 1982–83 El Niño, 90 percent of the fur seal pups in Peru died. In the same season, more than half of the elephant seal pups in California were lost due to storms that flooded pupping beaches (beaches where seals are born).

Seals in colonies on the California cost were especially hard hit during the 1997–98 El Niño. More than six thousand pups from a colony on San Miguel Island died by the end of 1997. The mortality rate of the pups reached 70 percent; in normal years just 25 percent of the young animals die.

Sea mammals were in such distress in 1997 and 1998 that animal rescue groups set up stations on California beaches. Members of these groups fed and cared for mammals they found stranded on beaches and sandbars. When the animals were well, rescuers released them back into the ocean.

At El Niño's peak in early 1998, water temperatures off Peru's Paracas Peninsula, normally 56 to 58°F (13 to 14°C), rose to 81 to 83°F (27 to 28°C). The results of this extreme warming could be witnessed in the thousands of sea lion and seal carcasses littering South America beaches from Chile to Ecuador.

Even the sea mammals as far away as Antarctica do not escape the grip of El Niño. The icy continent's weddell seal population declines significantly during El Niño years.

Runners on a beach near Lima, Peru, pass several dead Inca terns. Scientists believe that the sea birds died due to a shortage of food. AP IMAGES.

The 1982–83 El Niño

The El Niño of 1982 and 1983 was the second strongest El Niño in recorded history (second only to the 1998–99 event). The Southern Oscillation (shift in air pressure across the Pacific) was so great that the trade winds not only weakened, they reversed. Storms took the lives of more than 2,000 people and caused between thirteen and fifteen billion dollars in damage worldwide. El Niño brought about devastating droughts, floods, and storms in every continent except Antarctica.

Hawaii, Mexico, northeastern Brazil, southern Africa, the Philippines, India, Australia, and Indonesia all experienced droughts—some had brush fires and dust storms. Australia was hit with its worst drought ever. A dust storm swept more than 100,000 tons of soil from farmland into coastal cities and the ocean, and 60 percent of Australian farms experienced crop loss. Bush fires killed 72 people and more than 300,000 livestock.

Meanwhile, extensive flooding plagued the southwestern United States, the Gulf states, Cuba, Ecuador, Peru, and Bolivia. Five hurricanes pounded the islands of French Polynesia, and one hurricane blew through Hawaii.

The damage toll due to El Niño in Peru, Chile, Ecuador, Bolivia, and Colombia reached six billion dollars. Peru had its greatest rainfall in recorded history; some areas received sixty times more rain than normal. There were mud slides and flooding in the north and a drought in the south. The coastal town of Chulliyachi, in northwest Peru, was wiped off the map. Twenty-foot (six-meter) waves washed away the town church (it remains submerged along the coast today) and three residential blocks, and turned roads into rivers.

Galápagos Islands iguanas and penguins Another casualty of the warm El Niño waters is green algae. Green algae, which thrives in cold water, is the main food source of the marine iguana, a 39-inch-long reptile that lives on the Galápagos Islands. When the water warms, the green algae become stunted and covered with brown algae. Brown algae are not digestible by marine iguanas. During the 1982–83 El Niño, as the green algae went into decline, much of the Galápagos marine iguana population was wiped out. In 1998, when the waters warmed by 10°F (5.6°C), marine iguanas suffered again.

The penguins that live on the Galápagos Islands also suffer during El Niño. Galápagos penguins make their homes on several of the islands, including the northernmost islands, which are north of the equator. That makes these flightless birds, which measure twenty to twenty-four inches high and weigh four to five pounds, the sole penguin species naturally occurring in the Northern Hemisphere.

The town's 1,500 residents had to be airlifted to safety.

In Ecuador, El Niño rains caused landslides and washed away roads, bridges, houses, and farm animals. The rains drowned crops and destroyed the main railroad line leading to the capital city, Quito. The flooding in coastal Ecuador and northern Peru killed 600 people, mainly those living in slums.

Damage due to storms in the United States cost more than two billion dollars. A string of violent storms traveled across the west coast of the United States, drenching California and creating mud slides and floods and washing away beaches. More than thirty houses were washed off hillsides, into the ocean. There were also storms and flooding in the Rocky Mountains and the Gulf states. The East Coast had its warmest winter in twenty-five years, at a savings of 500 million dollars in heating bills.

Costs of the 1982-83 El Niño	
Droughts/Fires:	
Australia	$2.5B
Southern Africa	$1B
Mexico and Central America	$600M
Indonesia	$500M
Philippines	$450M
Southern Peru, Western Bolivia	$240M
Southern India, Sri Lanka	$150M
Flooding:	
U.S. Gulf States	$1.27B
Ecuador, Northern Peru	$650M
Bolivia	$300M
Cuba	$170M
Hurricanes:	
Hawaii	$230M
Tahiti (French Polynesia)	$50M

The staple of the penguins' diet is small fish, primarily mullet. Those fish are driven away from the islands by warm El Niño waters. Since the nearest land is 600 miles away, penguins are unable to migrate in search of food. During the 1998 El Niño researchers observed skin-and-bones adult penguins and no juveniles—suggesting either that the birds did not breed or, if they did breed, all of the chicks died.

In the aftermath of the El Niños of 1982–83 and 1997–98, the Galápagos penguin population has been reduced to half its 1970 size. At the end of 1998, they numbered less than 8,500.

Secondary effects on land animals   El Niño's effects are felt by various species of land animals, namely those that feed upon marine animals and those whose habitats are affected by the changes in weather conditions. An example of a land animal that declines in number during El Niño years is the red fox. Red foxes that live on Round Island, Alaska, subsist mainly on the sea birds that nest there. When the warm waters appear and

the fish disappear, the population of sea birds—especially common murres and black-legged kittiwakes—declines. El Niño's effect on the foxes is evident in their reduced numbers of offspring. In normal years the foxes have up to seven litters, with four or more pups per litter. In El Niño years foxes typically have just one litter of three or four pups.

Some animal species are harmed by drought-induced wildfires during El Niño years. For the animals that inhabit the Indonesian islands of Borneo and Sumatra, the results of the 1997–98 El Niño were disastrous. At least six million acres of rain forest burned, driving out or killing thousands of orangutans and other animals. Across the Pacific in drought-struck Mexico, fires also burned. Those fires destroyed the winter habitat of monarch butterflies. The monarchs either died or made their home elsewhere.

Effects of El Niño on human health   Unusual weather produced by El Niño affects the health of human beings in many ways. For instance, hunger is a problem in areas where crops have failed due to drought. Respiratory ailments are common in regions ravaged by forest fires. Many diseases are spread by organisms that reproduce rapidly during El Niño years.

Cholera, dysentery, and typhoid are diseases that commonly spread during floods, when sewage treatment systems become overloaded and drinking water supplies become contaminated. An overabundance of standing water also enhances the breeding of mosquitoes, which carry malaria, dengue fever, yellow fever, and encephalitis (pronounced en-SEF-a-LIE-tus).

During the 1982–83 El Niño, flooding in Ecuador, Bolivia, Colombia, Peru, India, and Sri Lanka resulted in significant outbreaks of malaria. In early 1998, when El Niño–driven rains produced flooding, Peru experienced a malaria epidemic. In the Piura region of northwest Peru, where 1.5 million people reside, there were some 30,000 cases of malaria.

Also in 1983, the unusually mild and moist spring and summer in California gave rise to record numbers of fleas carrying the bubonic plague, an infectious disease that wiped out one-fourth of Europe's population during the Middle Ages (476–1453). Fleas spread the disease to mammals, which can pass on the illness to humans. In 1983, thirty-six people contracted the plague (all in western states), and six of them died. That outbreak was the most severe in the United States since the 1920s.

Another way that El Niño affects human health was discovered in 1993, following the outbreak of a deadly disease in the southwestern United States. The disease, caused by a type of virus called hantavirus, killed several people in the Four Corners region (the place where Arizona, Utah, Colorado, and New Mexico come together).

The hantavirus is carried by desert-dwelling rodents called deer mice. In normal years, the deer mouse population is small. Food for the rodents is in limited supply; and predators, such as owls and snakes, keep deer mouse numbers down. During the 1992 El Niño, however, the desert in the Four Corners region received a lion's share of rain. Plant life exploded, as did the deer mouse population.

Along with the greater numbers of deer mice came greater numbers of deer mouse droppings. People who either touched the droppings or breathed dust contaminated with the droppings risked exposure to the hantavirus. When the rains stopped and the desert returned to its arid state, the hantavirus outbreak subsided.

Warm El Niño waters threaten green algae, the main food source of the marine iguana.
©ROYALTY-FREE/CORBIS.

Did you know: El Niño bleaches coral reefs

Coral reefs, which are undersea ecosystems sometimes referred to as the rain forests of the oceans, are among the most species-rich places on Earth. Coral reefs are colonies of coral polyps (pronounced PALL-ups)—small, tube-shaped animals with hard exterior skeletons coated with colorful algae. The algae, which give the coral reefs the appearance of underwater gardens, are essential to the survival of the polyps.

Coral reefs are found in the warm, shallow waters of tropical oceans and can survive only within a small temperature range. An increase in temperature of just a few degrees can kill the algae. When the algae die, the coral bleaches (turns a whitish color). Bleaching typically leads to the death of a polyp colony.

Many coral reefs were bleached during the 1982–83 El Niño, when eastern Pacific Ocean temperatures increased by 4 to 5°F (2 to 3°C). Some coral species were wiped out entirely. The most extensive damage to coral reefs occurred off the coasts of the Galápagos Islands, Ecuador, Colombia, Panama, and Costa Rica. There the losses to three-hundred-year-old coral reefs ranged from 50 to 97 percent. Scientists estimate that it will take centuries for the corals in those areas to recover.

The bleaching of corals recurred during the 1997–98 El Niño. Significant damage was done to the reefs off the Pacific coasts of Panama, Costa Rica, and Mexico. The warm waters also wiped out an 18-mile (29-kilometer) long coral colony along the Great Barrier Reef of Australia. Varying degrees of bleaching also occurred in coral reefs off the coasts of French Polynesia, Kenya, the Galápagos Islands, the Florida Keys, Baja California, Mexico's Yucatan coast, the Cayman Islands, and the Netherlands Antilles. The corals at most of these sites were expected to recover once the water temperature returned to normal.

During the El Niño of 1997–98, the desert again received exceptional rainfall. With conditions ripe for a deer mouse population increase, the local population was instructed to steer clear of the rodents and their droppings.

The human factor: A possible link between El Niño and global warming

The strongest El Niños on record occurred in the 1980s and 1990s. That reality has prompted scientists to consider whether human activity—namely global warming—has an effect on El Niño.

Average temperatures around the world have risen over the last 100 years. Global warming is the theory that temperatures have begun to rise, and will continue to rise, due to an increase of certain gases, called

Orangutans struggle to survive

The effects of the 1997–98 El Niño pushed orangutans toward possible extinction. Orangutans that survived the wildfires brought about by the El Niño–induced drought in Indonesia faced starvation due to dwindling food sources. Baby orangutans, too weak to hold onto their mothers, reportedly dropped from trees and died. Prior to the wildfires, orangutans were already considered an endangered species (their population had been reduced by forest clearing and hunting).

The 1997–98 El Niño contributed to diminished populations of orangutans in Indonesia. ©W. PERRY CONWAY/ CORBIS.

greenhouse gases, in the atmosphere. Greenhouse gases are gases that trap heat in the atmosphere. The most abundant greenhouse gases are water vapor and carbon dioxide. Others include methane, nitrous oxide, and chlorofluorocarbons. The atmospheric increase of one particular greenhouse gas—carbon dioxide—is believed to be the primary reason for global warming. Carbon dioxide is produced by the burning of fossil fuels. It is emitted by factory smokestacks and cars.

Over the last century, the amount of carbon dioxide released into the atmosphere has increased by 30 percent. During that same time period, the planet has become, on average, slightly more than $1°F$ ($0.5°C$) warmer. The warmest year in U.S. history since the keeping of detailed records began in 1895 was 1998. The years 1997 and 1998 were the world's warmest two years of the last century.

The Intergovernmental Panel on Climate Change (IPCC), a group consisting of 2,500 of the world's leading climatologists, believes that the balance of evidence suggests that humans do have an effect on global climate. The question remains: Is that human influence affecting El Niño?

Arguments for and against the global warming connection   Scientists were prompted to look at a possible connection between global warming and El Niño when the 1997–98 El Niño showed itself as the strongest episode in recorded history, just two years after the end of a five-year El Niño—the longest episode in recorded history. In addition, the 1997–98 El Niño came just fourteen years after the 1982–83 El Niño—previously the strongest episode on record. According to statistical models, such a sequence would occur naturally just once every two thousand years. That fact suggests that human-induced factors, rather than nature, may be responsible for the pair of unusually strong El Niños.

One theory explaining how global warming and increased El Niño activity are connected is that as the planet warms, heat builds up in the Pacific Ocean. El Niño acts as an escape valve for the excess heat, moving it eastward across the ocean and then releasing it into the atmosphere. Furthermore, computer simulations (computer programs that mimic real-world events) show that increased carbon dioxide levels in the atmosphere lead to an uneven heating of the planet. In the Pacific Ocean, the eastern portion warms to a greater degree than the western portion (exactly the conditions found during El Niño).

While many scientists believe that global warming may affect El Niño, few believe that is the entire reason. El Niño experts point out that huge shifts have occurred in the global climate over the past hundreds of thousands of years, without any human influence such as global warming. Natural variability in climate has ranged from ice ages to warm periods. At certain times in our planet's past, El Niño–like conditions have lasted for thousands of years.

Many scientists refuse to make conclusions about the impact of global warming on El Niño based on one century's worth of data. Those scientists argue that at least another century of careful measurement of El Niños is needed to make such a determination.

Why most scientists won't yet blame global warming While many scientists think that global warming may affect El Niño, few think there is sufficient evidence to be certain. El Niño experts point to the huge shifts that the global climate has experienced over the past hundreds of thousands of years, without the influence of humans. They refuse to make assessments based on spotty data from one century. (Detailed data collection on El Niño around the world only began in 1986.) They suggest that the recent series of unusually strong El Niños may be within normal limits of shifts in global climate.

One reason why it may be too early to blame global warming for increased El Niño activity is that there are many, many influences on global climate, most of them unrelated to human activity. Throughout the Earth's history, the natural variability in climate has ranged from ice ages to warm periods. At certain times in our planet's past, El Niño–like conditions have lasted for thousands of years.

Many members of the scientific community think that at least another century of careful measurement of El Niños is needed to determine whether or not global warming is a factor.

Why are a few degrees of warming such a big deal? You may be wondering why a warming of the ocean of just a few degrees has such a tremendous impact on weather. After all, slight changes in air temperature happen frequently with little consequence. In the case of El Niño, it is the heat contained in a tremendous volume of water (twenty to thirty times as much water as all the Great Lakes combined) that matters. A temperature increase of even 1˚F throughout that volume of water results in a significant increase in the heat contained therein.

To understand El Niño's power, it is important to realize that heat and temperature are not the same thing. The difference between heat and temperature has to do with kinetic energy, the energy of motion. As molecules heat up, their kinetic energy increases. Heat is the total kinetic energy of a substance, whereas temperature is the average kinetic energy (also defined as the hotness or coldness) of a substance. In other words, heat takes into account the volume of a substance. If you take two volumes of liquid at the same temperature—say a bathtub and a coffee cup—the bathtub contains more heat.

Just how much kinetic energy does El Niño contain? It contains more energy than can be produced in one year by one million power plants, at 1,000 megawatts each; more energy than all the fossil fuel (gasoline, coal, and natural gas) that has burned in the United States since 1900; and as much energy as 500,000 twenty-megaton hydrogen bombs.

Technology connection: Predicting El Niños

Scientists have spent decades unlocking the secrets of El Niño and the Southern Oscillation. Now that a high level of understanding of these phenomena has been achieved, the most pressing task is predicting when they will occur. With advance warning of destructive weather, societies can make preparations to minimize the damage.

Predictions of El Niños remain of a general nature, such as whether conditions will be wetter, drier, colder, or warmer than usual. Crop growing season forecasts issued by international climate prediction agencies state one of the following: near-normal conditions; a weak El Niño with a slightly wetter than normal growing season; a full-blown El Niño with flooding; or cooler than normal waters offshore, with higher than normal chance of drought (in other words, La Niña conditions).

In recent years scientists have developed the tools to make predictions about the development, intensity, and effects of El Niño. They use a combination of computer models and measurements of air and water conditions in the tropical Pacific Ocean. The measurements are taken by a network of weather buoys (drifting or anchored floating objects containing weather instruments) and satellites, supplemented by readings taken on ships. With today's technology, meteorologists (scientists who study weather and climate) at weather prediction centers are able to observe changes in the ocean as they occur.

Computer-based prediction Beginning in the early 1980s, meteorologists have used computer models of climate change (also called climate modeling) in their attempts to predict El Niños. Climate modeling starts with a sophisticated computer program, called a numerical prediction model. The model incorporates mathematical equations that mimic processes in nature. The equations are based on the laws of oceanic and atmospheric physics, describing motion, thermodynamics (the relation of heat and mechanical energy), and the behavior of water.

When a set of data describing current conditions is entered into the computer, the program tells what is likely to happen up to several months in the future. The computer models are constantly fine-tuned based on data from the weather buoys and satellites.

Tropical Ocean-Global Atmosphere (TOGA) In the early 1980s the World Meteorological Organization, a Geneva, Switzerland–based agency of the United Nations, developed an ocean-monitoring system called the Tropical Ocean-Global Atmosphere (TOGA). The stated purpose of TOGA was to explore the predictability of the tropical ocean-atmosphere system and the impact on the global atmospheric climate on time scales of months to years. The development of TOGA was hastened by the strong 1982–83 El Niño, which took place during the planning stages of TOGA.

TOGA was coordinated by the National Oceanic and Atmospheric Administration (NOAA) of the United States and weather agencies of France, Japan, Korea, and Taiwan, with the participation of thirteen other nations. The program operated from 1985 to 1994. During that time TOGA researchers observed interactions between the air and sea in the equatorial Pacific and assessed how those interactions would affect changes in climate around the world.

TOGA used the following equipment to collect information: weather buoys, satellites, ships, and tidal gauges (instruments that measure the

Watch this: "Chasing El Niño"

In 1998, the PBS series NOVA broadcast an episode entitled "Chasing El Niño" that chronicles scientists' attempts to understand the causes of El Niño and make predictions on the magnitude and development of El Niño events. The documentary opens with a look at the Pacific Ocean, which is the largest feature of Earth's surface and has a huge influence on global climate. The program explores the history of El Niño prediction efforts in the Pacific, including the creation of the Tropical Atmosphere Ocean (TAO) array, a massive network of ocean buoys.

"Chasing El Niño" also explores the creation of the massive computer models scientists use to help predict El Niño's intensity. For those with a taste for more hands-on work, meteorologists are shown flying a plane directly into an oncoming storm! The scientists measure rainfall, temperature, wind speed, and air pressure in hopes of forecasting where the storm will fall. "Chasing El Niño" offers an informative and exciting look at the science of predicting one of the world's most mysterious weather effects.

Scientists adjust sensors on a TOGA-TAO buoy.

coming and goings of the tides). These instruments, collectively, measured water temperature at the ocean surface and to a depth of 1,650 feet (500 meters), as well as air temperature, relative humidity, ocean currents, sea level, and the speed and direction of surface winds. All data was transmitted daily, via satellite, to weather prediction centers.

Of the weather buoys, some were drifting and some were moored (anchored to the ocean floor). The drifting buoys, called Global Lagrangian Drifters, emitted signals that indicated their positions, and thus the direction of surface water motion. They also recorded air pressure and temperature of surface ocean water at various locations. The moored buoys measured surface winds and temperatures at various depths of the ocean.

The information collected by TOGA filled in many gaps of knowledge about El Niño's life cycle. The program also established the first means of monitoring the Pacific Ocean and the atmosphere in real time (at the present).

Tropical Atmosphere Ocean Array (TAO) Although the TOGA program ended in 1994, it initiated a permanent, international network of ocean-atmosphere monitoring. That system—which includes moored and drifting buoys, satellites, and research ships—is called the El Niño–Southern Oscillation Monitoring System. The central element of the monitoring system is the Tropical Atmosphere Ocean Array (TAO). Completed in December 1994 as TOGA was coming to an end, the TAO takes continuous ocean measurements. The purpose of the TAO is to detect El Niños in their earliest stages and improve forecasting.

One of TOGA's greatest achievements was the development of the TAO array. The TAO project is jointly coordinated by the NOAA and weather agencies in Japan, Taiwan, and France. Its headquarters are at the NOAA's Pacific Marine Environmental Laboratory (PMEL) in Seattle, Washington.

The TAO array consists of sixty-five moored buoys and five current meters (instruments that measure the strength and direction of currents), spanning the equatorial Pacific—covering one-third of the globe. The buoys and meters are stationed at intervals between longitudes of 135° east (near Indonesia) and 95° west (just west of Peru), and latitudes 10° north and 10° south (forming a wide band with the equator in the center). (Degrees of longitude are imaginary lines encircling Earth, perpendicular to the equator, that tell one's position east or west on the globe; degrees of latitude run parallel to the equator and tell one's position north or south on the globe).

TAO's buoys detect air temperature, surface wind speed and direction, relative humidity, sea surface temperature, and ocean temperature to a depth of 1,650 feet (500 meters). The buoys and current meters transmit information, via NOAA satellites, continuously to TAO project headquarters. The data is fed into high-speed computers and is analyzed, after which it is made available to weather prediction centers and climate researchers around the world.

TAO's computers combine the thousands of continuous readings from the buoys into a single picture. That picture appears on researchers' monitors as a checkerboard with different colored squares. The color of each square indicates the instruments' readings of ocean and atmosphere at a given location. New readings are entered, and the picture is updated several times a day. It is possible to view a series of pictures taken previously, in rapid succession—like a movie of ocean conditions. This technology allows researchers to literally watch El Niños unfold.

ATLAS buoys The TAO array's moored instruments are called ATLAS buoys. At the top of each buoy is a set of sensors measuring wind, humidity, and temperature; a data transmitter; and a satellite antenna. Beneath the floating portion of an ATLAS buoy hangs a 1,722-foot-long (525-meter-long) sensor cable. Temperature sensors are placed at various depths along the length of the cable. The cable ends with a 4,200-pound (1,900-kilogram) anchor.

Exploring: Take a virtual cruise on a research ship

A vital element of the TAO array is the National Oceanic and Atmospheric Association's (NOAA) research ship, the *Ka'imimoana* (means "ocean seeker"). The *Ka'imimoana* performs maintenance on the TAO's weather buoys. Scientists aboard the ship also take measurements of ocean currents, surface water temperature, and ocean temperature to depths of 4,957 feet (1500 meters).

The *Ka'imimoana* was constructed in 1989 and purchased by the NOAA in 1993. After being converted to an oceanic research vessel, the *Ka'imimoana* went into operation in April 1996.

Visit the *Ka'imimoana* home page at http://www.moc.noaa.gov/ka/index.html. There you will see the ship's officers and crew as well as photographs and data from the ship.

If governments are aware that unusual conditions will lead to crop loss or shortages of drinking water, they may stockpile food and water for their residents. Health precautions may be taken in areas where flooding is expected to produce outbreaks of waterborne or mosquito-borne diseases.

Predictions are also useful along the west coasts of South and North America, where high waves and flooding cause damage. If an El Niño is predicted, residents may build barriers to prevent beach erosion and work to reinforce bridges and other structures. At the same time, they may halt new construction projects.

The original ATLAS buoys had a life expectancy of one year, after which they required servicing or replacing. A new generation of ATLAS buoys was introduced in 1996, boasting longer lifetimes and greater measurement capabilities.

What's next for TAO The next phase in the prediction of El Niño will likely involve expanding the TAO array to the Indian Ocean, the tropical Atlantic Ocean, and throughout the northern and southern Pacific. Evidence indicates that climate variability in those regions is linked to El Niño. An NOAA program called the Pilot Research Moored Array (PIRATA) proposes to place buoys across the equatorial Atlantic Ocean early in the twenty-first century.

TOPEX/Poseidon satellite The TOPEX/Poseidon (TOPEX stands for Ocean Topography Experiment) satellite is another key player on the El Niño prediction team. This satellite—a joint project of the U.S. National Aeronautics and Space Agency (NASA) and the French space agency, Centre Nationale d'Etudes Spatiales (National Center of Space Studies)—was launched in 1992.

The TOPEX/Poseidon, orbiting the Earth at a height of 830 miles (1,336 kilometers), uses radar altimeters (instruments that measure altitude by bouncing radar beams off the ocean surface) to measure sea level heights. The measurements are accurate to within a few centimeters. Sea-surface heights are directly related to the heat content of the ocean. A rising sea level in the eastern Pacific is an important clue that an El Niño is underway.

The United States and France put into orbit another oceanographic (pertaining to the study of oceans) satellite in May 2000. The satellite replaced the TOPEX/Poseidon, which has lasted far longer than expected.

The benefits of El Niño prediction Once El Niño has been predicted, the challenge to researchers is how to make that prediction meaningful. The question for many experts is how El Niño predictions can be adapted to the needs of specific industries and people.

The task of making El Niño predictions useful has been assigned to the International Research Institute for Climate Prediction. That institute was established in 1996 at Columbia University's Lamont-Doherty Earth Observatory.

With advance warning of the destructive weather El Niño has in store, societies can make preparations to minimize the damage. El Niño predictions are most valuable to people involved in agriculture and fishing, especially in tropical nations. (The tropics generally suffer the greatest consequences of El Niño's droughts and flooding.) Other areas in which El Niño predictions are useful are public health, transportation, forestry, water resources, and energy production.

Among the countries that have used El Niño predictions to manage agriculture are Peru, Australia, Brazil, Ethiopia, and India. Farmers in these countries consider the expected precipitation levels and temperature when deciding which crops, and how much of each crop, to plant.

An example of the difference an El Niño prediction can make is the improvement in northeastern Brazilian agricultural yields in 1991 over those of 1987. Farmers in the state of Ceara in northeastern Brazil, in a typical year, produce 716,000 tons of rice, beans, and corn. In 1987 the region suffered from an El Niño–related drought, and crop production fell drastically to 110,000 tons. In 1991, in contrast, farmers heeded warnings of an impending El Niño–related drought. Government officials provided seeds that were drought-resistant and had shorter growing seasons, to willing farmers. As a result, 584,000 tons of crops were harvested.

A key reference to: El Niño warning signs

When any of the following trends are recorded by weather buoys or satellites, researchers take note that an El Niño may be brewing:

- The temperature of the surface water increases at progressively eastward locations.
- The water at great depths of the western Pacific cools (in other words, the pool of warm water in the western Pacific grows shallower).
- The air pressure in the western Pacific rises, or the air pressure in the eastern Pacific falls.
- The sea level in the western Pacific falls, or the sea level in the central or eastern Pacific rises.
- The speed of the easterly (from east to west) winds in the eastern Pacific decreases.
- The current, which typically runs from east to northwest, shifts direction.
- The relative humidity (amount of moisture in the air) falls over the western Pacific or rises over the central or eastern Pacific.

Farmers and fishermen in northern Peru made the most of predictions issued in advance of the 1997–98 El Niño. Anticipating heavy rains and the grass that would grow on normally dry land, farmers raised cattle. Farmers also planted rice—a crop that thrives in wet conditions (during dry years, in contrast, farmers may plant cotton—a crop that requires little rain). Fishermen planned for a harvest of shrimp, since those marine animals inhabit the warm waters that El Niño brings.

[*See Also* **Human Influences on Weather and Climate; Weather: An Introduction**]

For More Information

BOOKS

Arnold, Caroline. *El Niño: Stormy Weather for People and Wildlife.* New York: Clarion Books, 1998. Reprint, New York: NY, Clarion Books, 2005.

Fagan, Brian. *Floods, Famines and Emperors: El Niño and the Fate of Civilizations.* New York: Basic Books, 2000.

Glantz, Michael H. *Currents of Change: El Niño's Impact on Climate and Society.* 2nd ed. New York: Cambridge University Press, 2001.

Glynn, P. W., ed. *Global Ecological Consequences of the 1982–83 El Niño–Southern Oscillation.* Amsterdam: Elsevier Science Publishers, 1990.

WEB SITES

"El Niño." *National Oceanic and Atmospheric Administration.* <http://www.elnino.noaa.gov/> (accessed August 25, 2006).

"El Niño Resources." *USA Today.* <http://www.usatoday.com/weather/resources/basics/wnino0.htm> (accessed August 25, 2006).

"Tracking El Niño." *Nova Online.* <http://www.pbs.org/wgbh/nova/elnino/> (accessed August 25, 2006).

Where to Learn More

Books

Abbott, Patrick Leon, ed. *Natural Disasters.* 6th ed. Columbus, OH: McGraw-Hill Higher Education, 2008.

Aguado, Edward, and James Burt. *Understanding Weather and Climate.* 4th ed. Englewood Cliffs, NJ: Prentice Hall, 2006.

Ahrens, C. Donald. *Meteorology Today: An Introduction to Weather, Climate, and the Environment.* 7th ed. Belmont, CA: Thomson Brooks/Cole, 2006.

Allaby, Michael. *Blizzards.* 2nd ed. New York: Facts on File, 2003.

Allaby, Michael. *How the Weather Works: 100 Ways Parents and Kids Can Share the Secrets of the Atmosphere.* New York: Putnam Group, Inc., 1999.

Allen, Leslie, et. al. *Raging Forces: Earth in Upheaval.* Washington, DC: National Geographic Society, 1996.

Andryszewski, Tricia. *The Dust Bowl: Disaster on the Plains.* Brookfield, CT: The Millbrook Press, 1993.

Anthes, Richard A. *Meteorology,* 7th ed. New York: Prentice Hall, 1996.

Arnold, Caroline. *El Niño: Stormy Weather for People and Wildlife.* New York: Clarion Books, 2005.

Bair, Frank E. *Climates of States.* 5th ed. Farmington Hills, MI: Thomson Gale, 2007.

Binhua, Wang. *Sea Fog.* New York: Springer-Verlag, 1985.

Bolt, Bruce A. *Earthquakes.* 4th ed. Salt Lake City, UT: W. H. Freeman and Co., 1999.

Botkin, Daniel, and Edward Keller. *Environmental Science: Earth as a Living Planet.* 4th ed. Hoboken, NJ: John Wiley & Sons, Inc. 2004.

Breen, Mark, Kathleen Friestad, and Michael Kline. *The Kid's Book of Weather Forecasting: Build a Weather Station, 'Read' the Sky & Make Predictions!* Charlotte, VT: Williamson Publishing Company, 2000.

Brinkley, Douglas. *The Great Deluge: Hurricane Katrina, New Orleans, and the Mississippi Gulf Coast.* New York: William Morrow, 2006.

Bronson, William. *The Earth Shook, the Sky Burned.* San Francisco, CA: Chronicle Books, 1997.

Burroughs, William J., Bob Crowder, et. al. *Nature Company Guides: Weather.* New York: Time Life Books, 2000.

Campbell, N. A. *Biology.* 4th ed. Menlo Park, CA: The Benjamin/Cummings Publishing Company, Inc., 1996.

Carr, Michael. *International Marine's Weather Predicting Simplified: How to Read Weather Charts and Satellite Images.* New York: McGraw-Hill, 1999.

Chambers, Catherine. *Thunderstorm.* 2nd ed. Portsmouth, NH: Heinemann, 2007.

Chernov, Y. I. *The Living Tundra.* West Nyack, NY: Cambridge University Press, 1988.

Christian, Spencer, and Antonia Felix. *Shake, Rattle, and Roll: The World's Most Amazing Earthquakes, Volcanoes, and Other Forces.* New York: John Wiley & Sons, Inc., 1997.

Colten, Craig E. *An Unnatural Metropolis: Wrestling New Orleans from Nature.* Baton Rouge: Louisiana State University Press, 2005.

Cotton, William R., and Roger A. Pielke, Sr. *Human Impacts on Weather and Climate.* 2nd ed. New York: Cambridge University Press, 2007.

Dasch, E. Julius, ed. *Encyclopedia of Earth Sciences.* New York: Macmillan Library Reference, 1996.

De Blij, Harm J., et al. *Nature on the Rampage.* Washington, DC: Smithsonian Institution, 1994.

De Blij, Harm J., et al. *Restless Earth.* Washington, DC: National Geographic Society, 1997.

De Villiers, Marq. *Windswept: The Story of Wind and Weather.* New York: Walker & Company, 2006.

DeMillo, Rob. *How Weather Works.* Emeryville, CA: Ziff-Davis Press, 1994.

Drake, Frances. *Global Warming: The Science of Climate Change.* New York: Oxford University Press, 2000.

Drohan, Michele Ingber. *Avalanches.* New York: Rosen Publishing and PowerKids Press, 1999.

Drohan, Michele Ingber. *Floods.* New York: Rosen Publishing and PowerKids Press, 1999.

Fagan, Brian. *Floods, Famines and Emperors: El Niño and the Fate of Civilizations.* New York: Basic Books, 2000.

Ferguson, Sue, and Edward R. LaChapelle. *The ABCs of Avalanche Safety.* 3rd ed. Seattle, WA: Mountaineers Books, 2003.

Fisher, David E. *The Scariest Place on Earth: Eye to Eye with Hurricanes.* New York: Random House, 1994.

Flannery, Tim. *The Weather Makers: How Man Is Changing the Climate and What It Means for Life on Earth.* New York: Atlantic Monthly Press, 2006.

Frater, Alexander. *Chasing the Monsoon.* New York: Picador, 2005.

Geiger, Rudolf. *The Climate Near the Ground,* Cambridge, MA: Harvard University Press, 1965.

Gemmell, Kathy. *Storms and Hurricanes.* London: Usborne Publishing Ltd., 1996.

Glantz, Michael H. *Currents of Change: El Niño's Impact on Climate and Society.* 2nd ed. New York: Cambridge University Press, 2001.

Gore, Al. *An Inconvenient Truth: The Planetary Emergency of Global Warming and What We Can Do About It.* 2nd ed. New York: Rodale Books, 2006.

Hamblyn, Richard. *The Invention of Clouds: How an Amateur Meteorologist Forged the Language of the Skies.* London: Pan MacMillan, 2001.

Hambrey, Michael, and Jürg Alean. *Glaciers.* 2nd ed. Cambridge, UK: Cambridge University Press, 2004.

Hamilton, Richard. *Avalanches: Nature's Fury.* Minneapolis, MN: Abdo and Daughters, 2005.

Hodgson, Michael. *Basic Essentials Weather Forecasting.* 3rd ed. Guilford, CT: Falcon, 2007.

Hopping, Lorraine Jean. *Wild Weather: Blizzards!* New York: Scholastic Inc., 1999.

Houghton, John. *Global Warming: The Complete Briefing.* Cambridge, UK: Cambridge University Press, 2004.

Houze, Robert A., Jr. *Cloud Dynamics.* San Diego, CA: Academic Press, Inc., 1994.

Hurt, R. Douglas. *The Dust Bowl: An Agricultural and Social History.* Chicago: Nelson-Hall, 1981.

Hyndman, Donald, and David Hyndman. *Natural Hazards and Disasters.* New York: Brooks Cole, 2005.

Kahl, Jonathan D. W. *Weather Watch: Forecasting the Weather.* Toronto: Monarch Books of Canada Limited, 2002.

Kolber, Elizabeth. *Field Notes from a Catastrophe: Man, Nature, and Climate Change.* New York: Bloomsbury USA, 2006.

Larsen, Erik. *Isaac's Storm.* New York: Vintage Books, 2000.

Lauber, Patricia. *Hurricanes: Earth's Mightiest Storms.* New York: Scholastic Press, 1996.

Libby, W. F. *Radiocarbon Dating.* 2nd ed. University of Chicago Press, 1955.

Linden, Eugene. *The Winds of Change: Climate, Weather, and the Destruction of Civilizations.* New York: Simon & Schuster, 2006.

Lydolph, Paul E. *The Climate of the Earth.* Lanham, MD: Rowman & Littlefield Publishers, Inc., 1985.

McPhee, John. *Annals of the Former World.* New York: Farrar, Straus & Giroux, 1999.

McPhee, John. *The Control of Nature*. New York: Farrar, Straus & Giroux, 1999.

Merrick, Patrick. *Avalanches*. Plymouth, MN: Child's World, 1998.

Mogil, H. Michael. *Tornadoes*. Saint Paul, MN: Voyageur Press, 2003.

Moran, Joseph M., and Lewis W. Morgan. *Essentials of Weather*. Englewood Cliffs, NJ: Prentice Hall, 1995.

Murck, Barbara W. *Dangerous Earth: An Introduction to Geologic Hazards*. New York: John Wiley & Sons, Inc., 1996.

Murphee, Tom, and Mary Miller, with the San Francisco Exploratorium. *Watching Weather: A Low Pressure Book about High Pressure Systems*. New York: Henry Holt and Company, 1998.

Nash, J. Madeleine. *El Niño: Unlocking the Secrets of the Master Weather-Maker*. New York: Warner Books, 2003.

National Geographic Society. *Restless Earth: Disasters of Nature*. Washington, DC: National Geographic Society, 1997.

The National Geographic Desk Reference. Washington, DC: National Geographic Society, 1999.

National Geographic Society and Ralph M. Feather, Jr. *Earth Science*. New York: Glencoe/McGraw-Hill, 2002.

O'Meara, Donna. *Into the Volcano: A Volcano Researcher at Work*. Tonawanda, NY: Kids Can Press, 2007.

Pearce, Fred. *When the Rivers Run Dry: Water—The Defining Crisis of the Twenty-First Century*. Boston, MA: Beacon Press, 2006.

Philander, S. George. *Our Affair with El Niño: How We Transformed an Enchanting Peruvian Current into a Global Climate Hazard*. Princeton, NJ: Princeton University Press, 2004.

Pretor-Pinney, Gavin. *The Cloudspotter's Guide*. New York: Perigee, 2006.

Reader's Digest Association, eds. *Great Disasters: Dramatic True Stories of Nature's Awesome Powers*. Pleasantville, NY: Reader's Digest, 1991.

Robinson, Andrew. *Earth Shock: Hurricanes, Volcanoes, Earthquakes, Tornadoes and Other Forces of Nature*. New York: W. W. Norton & Company, 2002.

Rosenfeld, Jeffrey P. *Eye of the Storm: Inside the World's Deadliest Hurricanes, Tornadoes, and Blizzards*. New York: Basic Books, 2005.

Rubin, Louis D., and Jim Duncan. *The Weather Wizard's Cloud Book*. Chapel Hill, NC: Algonquin Books of Chapel Hill, 1989.

Simon, Seymour. *Hurricanes*. New York: Harper Trophy, 2003.

Simon, Seymour. *Tornadoes*. New York: Harper Trophy, 2001.

Simon, Seymour. *Weather*. New York: Collins, 2006.

Stanley, Jerry. *Children of the Dust Bowl: The True Story of the School at Weedpatch Camp*. New York: Crown Publishers Inc., 1992.

Stewart, Gail. *Overview Series—Catastrophe in Southern Asia: The Tsunami of 2004.* San Diego, CA: Lucent Books, 2005.

Svobida, Lawrence. *Farming the Dust Bowl: A First-Hand Account from Kansas.* Lawrence, KS: University Press of Kansas, 1986. (Originally published in 1940 by The Caxton Printers, Ltd.)

Sweeney, Karen O'Connor. *Nature Runs Wild.* Danbury, CT: Franklin Watts Inc., 1979.

Tannenbaum, Beulah, and Harold E. Tannenbaum. *Making and Using Your own Weather Station.* New York: Franklin Watts, 1989.

Tibballs, Geoff. *Tsunami: The Most Terrifying Disaster.* London: Carlton Publishing Group, 2005.

Trewartha, Glenn T., and Lyle H. Horn. *An Introduction to Climate.* 5th ed. New York: McGraw-Hill, 1980.

VanCleave, Janice. *Earth Science for Every Kid: 101 Easy Experiments that Really Work.* New York: John Wiley, 1991.

Vasquez, Tim. *Weather Forecasting Handbook.* 5th ed. Garland, TX: Weather Graphics Technologies, 2002.

Verkaik, Jerrine, and Arjen Verkaik. *Under the Whirlwind: Everything You Need to Know About Tornadoes But Didn't Know Who to Ask.* 2nd ed., Elmwood, Ontario, Canada: Whirlwind Books, 2001.

Walker, Jane. *Avalanches and Landslides.* New York: Gloucester Press, 1992.

Walker, Jane. *Famine, Drought and Plagues.* New York: Gloucester Press, 1992.

Ward, Kaari, ed. *Great Disasters.* Pleasantville, NY: Reader's Digest Association, 1989.

Waterlow, Julia. *Violent Earth: Flood.* New York: Hodder Children's Books, 1994.

Watt, Fiona, and Francis Wilson. *Weather and Climate.* London: Usborne Publishing Ltd., 1992.

Williams, Jack. *The Weather Book: An Easy-to-Understand Guide to the USA's Weather.* New York: Vintage Books, 1997.

Worster, Donald. *Dust Bowl: The Southern Plains in the 1930s.* New York: Oxford University Press, 1979.

Wright, Richard T. *Environmental Science: Toward A Sustainable Future.* 10th ed. Upper Saddle River, NJ: Prentice Hall, 2007.

Zebrowski, Ernest, and Ernest Zebrowski Jr. *Perils of a Restless Planet: Scientific Perspectives on Natural Disasters.* Ann Arbor: University of Michigan Press, 2005.

Zebrowski, Ernest, and Judith A. Howard. *Category 5: The Story of Camille: Lessons Unlearned from America's Most Violent Hurricane.* Cambridge, UK: Cambridge University Press, 1999.

Periodicals

Ackerman, Jennifer. "Islands at the Edge." *National Geographic* (August 1997): pp. 2–31.

Akin, Wallace. "The Great Tri-State Tornado." *American Heritage* (May/June 2000): pp. 32–36.

Allen, Brian. "Capitol Hill Meltdown: While the Nation Sizzles, Congress Fiddles over Measures to Slow Down Future Climate Change." *Time* (August 9, 1999): p. 56+.

Annin, Peter. "Power on the Prairie: In Minnesota, They're Harvesting the Wind." *Newsweek* (October 26, 1998): p. 66.

Appenzeller, Tim. "The Case of the Missing Carbon." *National Geographic* (February, 2004): pp. 88–117.

Appenzeller, Tim. "Humans in the Hot Seat." *U.S. News & World Report* (November 6, 2000): p. 54.

Appenzeller, Tim, and Dennis R. Dimick. "Signs from Earth." *National Geographic* (September 2004): pp. 2–12.

"Avalanche!" *National Geographic World* (January 1997): pp. 2–6.

Baliunas, Sallie. "Full of Hot Air: A Climate Alarmist Takes on 'Criminals Against Humanity'." *Reason* (October 2005): p. 1.

Beardsley, Tim. "Dissecting a Hurricane." *Scientific American* (March 2000): pp. 80–85.

Begley, Sharon. "The Mercury's Rising." *Newsweek* (December 4, 2000): p. 52.

Bentley, Mace. "A Midsummer's Nightmare." *Weatherwise* (August/September 1996).

Bentley, Mace, and Steve Horstmeyer. "Monstrous Mitch." *Weatherwise* (March/April 1999).

Bishop, Ian D., and David R. Miller. "Visual Assessment Of Off-Shore Wind Turbines: The Influence of Distance, Contrast, Movement and Social Variables." *Renewable Energy: An International Journal* (April 2007): pp. 814–831.

Bond, Kathleen. "Church Backs Poor in Drought; Brazil's Leaders Slow to Respond." *National Catholic Reporter* (August 14, 1998): p. 11+.

Brenstein, Seth. "Hottest Years Ever Strengthen the Scientific Case for an Ever-Warming World." Knight-Ridder/Tribune News Service (January 13, 2000).

Brooks, Tim. "Fire and Rain: Forecasting the Chaos of Weather." *National Geographic* (June 2005): pp. 90–109.

Brown, Kathryn. "Invisible Energy." *Discover* (October 1999): p. 36.

Carroll, Chris. "In Hot Water." *National Geographic* (August 2005): pp. 72–85.

Chacon, Richard. "The Earth Calms, and Recovery Begins." *Boston Globe* (January 19, 2001): p. A13.

Coila, Bridget. "Changing the Weather." *Weatherwise* (May/June 2005): pp. 50–54.

Currie, Lloyd. "The Remarkable Metrological History of Radiocarbon Dating." *Journal of Research of the National Institute of Standards and Technology* (March/April 2004): pp. 185–217.

De Roy, Tui. "Caught in a Melting World." *International Wildlife* (November/December 2000): pp. 12–19.

Dick, Jason. "Global Warming." *Amicus Journal* (Summer 1999): p. 13.

"Drowning: Bangladesh." *The Economist* (September 12, 1998): p. 43.

Duffy, James A. "Administration Signs Global Warming Agreement." Knight-Ridder/Tribune News Service (November 12, 1998).

Dugger, Celia W. "2-Month Flood Breeds Havoc and Diseases in Bangladesh." *New York Times* (October 10, 1998): p. A9.

Dugger, Celia W. "Monsoon Hangs On, Swamping Bangladesh." *New York Times* (September 7, 1998): p. A1, A5.

Ehrlich, Gretel. "Last Days of the Ice Hunters." *National Geographic* (January 2006): pp. 79–101.

"Enviro-Cars: The Race Is On." *Business Week* (February 8, 1999): p. 74.

Favstovsky, D. E., and P. M. Sheehan. "The Extinction of the Dinosaurs in North America." *GSA Today* (March 2005): pp. 4–10.

"Fighting Global Warming with Iron at Sea." *Newsweek* (October 23, 2000): p. 54.

Findley, Rowe. "Mount St. Helens: Nature on Fast Forward." *National Geographic* (May 2000): pp. 106–125.

"Fire Forces 200 from Homes Near Boulder." *New York Times* (September 18, 2000): p. A22.

Fox, Stephen. "For a While…It Was Fun." *Smithsonian* (September 1999): pp. 128–130, 132, 134–140, 142.

Franklin, James L. "A Season of Devastation: Atlantic Hurricanes 2004." *Weatherwise* (March/April 2005): pp. 52–61.

Gaines, Ernest J. "Home No More." *National Geographic* (August 2006): pp. 42–53.

Glick, Daniel. "The Big Thaw." *National Geographic* (September 2004): pp. 13–33.

"Global Warming May Be Beneficial." *USA Today Magazine* (June 2000): p. 10.

Gonzalez, Frank I. "Tsumani!" *Scientific American* (May 1999): pp. 56–65.

Gore, Rick. "Andrew Aftermath." *National Geographic* (April 1993): pp. 2–37.

Griekspoor, Phyllis J. "Baked Kansas: La Niña Heralds a Possible Drought for State." *Wichita Eagle* (February 2006).

Grove, Noel. "Volcanoes: Crucibles of Creation." *National Geographic* (December 1992): pp. 5–41.

Halverson, Jeffrey B. "Chasing Hurricanes in Africa." *Weatherwise* (November/December 2006): pp. 62–64.

Halverson, Jeffrey B. "A Climate Conundrum." *Weatherwise* (March/April 2006): pp. 18–23.

Halverson, Jeffrey B. "A Hurricane Is Born." *Weatherwise* (November/December 2004): pp. 72–73.

Hanson-Harding, Alexandra. "Global Warming." *Junior Scholastic* (November 27, 2000): p. 6.

Hayden, Thomas. "Super Storms: No End in Sight." *National Geographic* (August 2006): pp. 66–77.

Hebert, H. Josef. "Scientists Paint Grim View of Impact on U.S. of Global Warming." Associated Press (June 9, 2000).

Helvarg, David. "Antarctica: The Ice Is Moving." *E* (September 2000): p. 33.

Henson, Robert. "Hot, Hotter, Hottest: 1998 Raised the Bar for Global Temperature Leaps." *Weatherwise* (March/April 1999): pp. 34–37.

Henson, Robert. "The Intensity Problem: How Strong Will a Hurricane Get?" *Weatherwise* (September/October 1998): pp. 20–26.

Hertsgaard, Mark. "Killer Weather Ahead." *Nation* (February 26, 2007): pp. 5–6.

Hodges, Glenn. "Russian Smokejumpers." *National Geographic* (August 2002): pp. 82–100.

"Hurricane Havoc in Central America." *The Economist* (November 7, 1998): p. 33.

"Hurricanes Rip Through Impoverished Caribbean, Central American Regions." *National Catholic Reporter* (November 20, 1998): p. 12.

"Iceland's Trial by Fire." *National Geographic* (May 1997): pp. 58–71.

Iocavelli, Debi. "Hurricanes: Eye Spy." *Weatherwise* (August/September 1996): pp. 10–11.

Keisterm, Edwin, Jr. " Battling the Orange Monster." *Smithsonian* (July 2000): pp. 32–42.

Klesius, Michael. "The Mystery of Snowflakes." *National Geographic* (January 2007): p. 22.

Lange, Karen. "Direct Hit: Inside a Tornado." *National Geographic* (June 2005): pp. 112–115.

Larsen, Josh. "The Emergence of the Weather Blog." *Weatherwise* (January/February 2007): pp. 10–11.

Lawless, Jill. "Global Warming Threatens a Third of World's Habitats." Associated Press (August 30, 2000).

Le Comte, Douglas. "Weather around the World." *Weatherwise* (March/April 2001): pp. 23–28.

Levine, Mark. "A Storm at the Bone: A Personal Exploration into Deep Weather." *Outside Magazine* (November 1998).

Libbrecht, Kenneth G. "The Formation of Snow Crystals." *American Scientist* (January/February 2007): pp. 52–59.

McDonald, Kim A. "Unearthing Earth's Ancient Atmosphere Beneath Two Miles of Greenland Ice." *Chronicle of Higher Education* (August 2, 1996): pp. A6+.

McKibbin, Warwick J., and Peter J. Wilcoxen. "Until We Know More About Global Warming, the Best Policy Is a Highly Flexible One." *Chronicle of Higher Education* (July 2, 1999): pp. B4+.

Mazza, Patrick. "Global Warming Is Here!" *Earth Island Journal* (Fall 1999): p. 14.

Mazza, Patrick. "The Invisible Hand: As Human Activity Warms the Earth, El Niño Grows More Violent." *Sierra* (May/June 1998): pp. 68+.

Miner, Todd, Peter J. Sousounis, James Wallman, and Greg Mann. "Hurricane Huron." *Bulletin of the American Meteorological Society* (February 2000): pp. 223–236.

Mitchell, Mitch. "Wind Gusts Cause Power Outages, Dust Storm." *Fort Worth Star-Telegram* (April 2006).

Montaigner, Fenck. "No Room to Run." *National Geographic* (September 2004): pp. 34–55.

Mulvaney, Kieran. "Alaska: The Big Meltdown." *E* (September 2000): p. 36.

Nielsen, Clifford H. "Hurd Willett: Forecaster Extraordinaire." *Weatherwise* (August/September 1993): pp. 38–44.

Nuttall, Nick. "Ganges Glacier Melting Fast." *The Times* (London). (July 20, 1999): p. 9.

Pearce, Fred. "Science: Meltdown in the Mountains." *The Independent* (London). (March 31, 2000): p. 8.

Perkins, S. "Greenland's Ice Is Thinner at the Margins." *Science News* (July 22, 2000): p. 54.

Peterson, Chester Jr. "Harvest the Wind: The Midwest Could Be the Saudi Arabia of Wind-Powered Energy." *Successful Farming* (January 1999): p. 44+.

Pinna, Marco. "Etna Ignites." *National Geographic* (February, 2002): pp. 68–87.

Proctor, Paul. "Fire-Fighting Fleet Stretched to Limit as U.S. West Burns." *Aviation Week & Space Technology* (August 21, 2000): pp. 38–39.

"Rain, Rain, Go Away . . . ." *Time International* (September 14, 1998): p. 18.

Rasicot, Julie. "Locals Help Battle Fires in Montana." *The Washington Post* (August 17, 2000): p. 16.

"Renewable Energy Resources." *Current Health 2* (April 1999): p. S14.

Revkin, Andrew C. "Treaty Talks Fail to Find Consensus in Global Warming." *New York Times* (November 26, 2000).

Rosenfeld, Jeff. "Mr. Tornado: The Life and Career of Ted Fujita." *Weatherwise* (May/June 1999): p. 18.

Rosenfeld, Jeff. "Sentinels in the Sky." *Weatherwise* (January/February 2000): pp. 24–27.

Rosenfeld, Jeff. "Unearthing Climate." *Weatherwise* (May/June 2000): p. 12.

Santana, Sofia. "Remembering Andrew." *Weatherwise* (July/August 2002): pp. 14–19.

Shepherd, Marshall. "The big picture: Satellites have changed our view of the world." *Weatherwise.* (January/February 2003): pp. 24–37.

Shilts, Elizabeth. "Harnessing a Powerful Breeze." *Canadian Geographic* (May/June 1999): p. 20.

Simpson, Sarah. "Raging Rivers of Rock." *Scientific American* (July 2000): pp. 24–25.

"The State of U.S. Renewable Power." *Mother Earth News* (February 1999): p. 16.

Stevens, William K. "Catastrophic Melting of Ice Sheet Is Possible, Studies Hint." *New York Times* (July 7, 1998): p. B13.

Stevens, William K. "Human Imprint on Climate Change Grows Clearer." *New York Times* (June 29, 1999): p. 1+.

Sudetic, Chuck. "As the World Burns." *Rolling Stone* (September 2, 1999): p. 97+.

Suplee, Curt. "El Niño/La Niña." *National Geographic* (March 1999): pp. 72–95.

Taylor, Jeff. "Flood Convergence." *Reason* (December 2005).

"That Dreadful Smog Is Back." *The Economist* (March 18, 2000): p. 40.

Trenberth, Kevin. "Uncertainty in Hurricanes and Global Warming." *Science* (17 June 2005): pp. 1753–1754.

Vesilind, Priit J. "The Hard Science, Dumb Luck, and Cowboy Nerve of Chasing Tornadoes." *National Geographic* (April 2004): pp. 2–37.

"U.S. Signs Kyoto Pact." *Maclean's* (November 23, 1998): p. 93.

Williams, A. R. "After the Deluge." *National Geographic* (November 1999): pp. 108–129.

Williams, A. R. "Popocatepetl: Mexico's Smoking Mountain." *National Geographic* (January 1999): pp. 116–137.

Williams, A. R. "Montserrat: Under the Volcano." *National Geographic* (July 1997): pp. 58–75.

Williams, Jack. "Antarctica: A Land of Ice and Wind." *Weatherwise* (January/February 2000): pp. 14–22.

Wunsch, Carl. "Quantitative Estimate of the Milankovitch-forced Contribution to Observed Quaternary Climate Change." *Quaternary Science Reviews* (Vol. 23, 2004):1001–1012.

Zwingle, Erla. "Meltdown: The Alps under Pressure." *National Geographic* (February, 2006): pp. 96–115.

Web Sites

Allgeyer, Robert. "APPENDIX: The Fata Morgana Mirage over Monterey Bay." *View to the Horizon.* <http://www.icogitate.com/~ergosum/essays/vtth/viewtothehorizon.htm> (accessed June 14, 2007).

American Avalanche Association. <http://www.americanavalancheassociation.org/> (accessed June 14, 2007).

"Avalanche!" *NOVA Online.* <http://www.pbs.org/wgbh/nova/avalanche/> (accessed June 14, 2007).

"Avalanche Awareness." *National Snow and Ice Data Center.* <http://nsidc.org/snow/avalanche/> (accessed June 14, 2007).

"Cascades Volcano Observatory." *United States Geological Survey.* <http://vulcan.wr.usgs.gov/> (accessed June 14, 2007).

"Climate Change." *United States Environmental Protection Agency.* <http://www.epa.gov/climatechange/> (accessed June 14, 2007).

"Climate Change." *World Wildlife Fund.* <http://www.panda.org/about_wwf/what_we_do/climate_change/index.cfm> (accessed June 14, 2007).

"Climate Change Impacts: Feeling the Heat." *Nature Conservancy.* <http://www.nature.org/initiatives/climatechange/issues> (accessed June 14, 2007).

Cowley, Les. "Rainbows." *Atmosphere Optics.* <http://www.atoptics.co.uk/rayshad.htm> (accessed June 14, 2007).

"Do-It-Yourself Weather Forecasting." *Weather Michigan.* <http://www.weathermichigan.com/u_do_it.htm> (accessed June 14, 2007).

"Driving in Fog." *California Highway Patrol.* <http://www.chp.ca.gov/html/fog-tips.html> (accessed June 14, 2007).

"Drought." *National Weather Service: Hydrologic Information Center.* <http://www.nws.noaa.gov/oh/hic/current/drought/> (accessed June 14, 2007).

"Drought Watch." *U.S. Geological Survey.* <http://water.usgs.gov/waterwatch/?m=dryw> (accessed June 14, 2007).

"El Niño." *National Oceanic and Atmospheric Administration.* <http://www.elnino.noaa.gov/> (accessed June 14, 2007).

"Flood." *Federal Emergency Management Agency.* <http://www.fema.gov/hazard/flood/index.shtm> (accessed June 14, 2007).

"Flood Safety." *National Weather Service Flood Safety.* <http://www.floodsafety.noaa.gov/> (accessed June 14, 2007).

"Forces and Winds: Online Meteorology Guide." *University of Illinois: Weather World 2010 Project.* <http://ww2010.atmos.uiuc.edu/(Gh)/guides/mtr/fw/home.rxml> (accessed June 14, 2007).

Geist, Eric L., and Laura Zink Torresan. "Life of a Tsunami." *United States Geological Survey.* <http://walrus.wr.usgs.gov/tsunami/basics.html> (accessed June 14, 2007).

"Hawaiian Volcano Observatory." *United States Geological Survey.* <http://hvo.wr.usgs.gov/> (accessed June 14, 2007).

Helmuth, Laura. "Antarctica Erupts!" *Smithsonian Science and Technology.* <http://www.smithsonianmag.com/issues/2006/december/antarctica.php> (accessed June 14, 2007).

"Historical Winter Storms." *The Weather Channel.* <http://www.weather.com/encyclopedia/winter/history.html> (accessed June 14, 2007).

"Hurricanes." *FEMA for Kids.* <http://www.fema.gov/kids/hurr.htm> (accessed June 14, 2007).

"Hurricanes." *National Oceanic and Atmospheric Administration.* <http://hurricanes.noaa.gov/>(accessed June 14, 2007).

Jaffe, Eric. "Volcanic Lightning." *Smithsonian Science and Technology.* <http://www.smithsonianmag.com/issues/2007/february/augustine.php> (accessed June 14, 2007).

"La Niña." *National Aeronautic and Space Administration: Earth Observatory.* <http://earthobservatory.nasa.gov/Library/LaNina/> (accessed June 14, 2007).

"La Niña." *National Oceanic and Atmospheric Administration.* <http://www.elnino.noaa.gov/lanina.html>(accessed June 14, 2007).

"Local Winds: Mountain Breezes." *Danish Wind Industry Association.* <http://www.windpower.org/en/tour/wres/mount.htm> (accessed June 14, 2007).

"The Monsoon." *National Weather Service.* <http://www.wrh.noaa.gov/fgz/science/monsoon.php?wfo=fgz> (accessed June 14, 2007).

"Names of Winds." *Golden Gate Weather Services.* <http://ggweather.com/winds.html> (accessed June 14, 2007).

"National Avalanche Center." *U.S. Forest Service.* <http://www.avalanche.org/%7enac/> (accessed June 14, 2007).

"National Hurricane Center Home Page." *National Hurricane Center.* <http://www.nhc.noaa.gov/> (accessed June 14, 2007).

"National Oceanic and Atmospheric Administration Home Page." *National Oceanic and Atmospheric Administration.* <http://www.noaa.org> (accessed June 14, 2007).

"Natural Hazards—Wildfires." *United States Geological Survey.* <http://www.usgs.gov/hazards/wildfires/> (accessed June 14, 2007).

"North American Monsoon Experiment (NAME)." *NASA Earth Observatory.* <http://earthobservatory.nasa.gov/Newsroom/Campaigns/NAME_Mission.html> (accessed June 14, 2007).

"NCAR/UCAR/UOP Home." *National Center for Atmospheric Research.* <http://www.ucar.edu/> (accessed June 14, 2007).

"Official Weather Forecasts and Warnings." *The World Meteorological Organization.* <http://www.wmo.int/> (accessed June 14, 2007).

Pacific Tsunami Museum. <http://www.tsunami.org/> (accessed June 14, 2007).

"Planet Earth." *NASA's Observatorium.* <http://observe.arc.nasa.gov/nasa/earth/earth_index.shtml.html> (accessed June 14, 2007).

"Thunderstorms and Lightning." *Federal Emergency Management Administration.* <http://www.fema.gov/hazard/thunderstorm/index.shtm> (accessed June 14, 2007).

"Tornado." *Federal Emergency Management Administration.* <http://www.fema. gov/hazard/tornado/index.shtm> (accessed June 14, 2007).

"Tsunamis." *Coastal Ocean Institute.* <http://www.whoi.edu/institutes/coi/view Topic.do?o=readid=281> (accessed June 14, 2007).

"U.S. Drought Monitor." *University of Nebraska, Lincoln.* <http://www.drought. unl.edu/dm/monitor.html> (accessed June 14, 2007).

"Wave that Shook the World." *NOVA.* <http://www.pbs.org/wgbh/nova/ tsunami/> (accessed June 14, 2007).

"Weather." *National Oceanic and Atmospheric Administration.* <http://www. noaa.gov/wx.html> (accessed June 14, 2007).

"Weather Office." *Environment Canada.* <http://weatheroffice.ec.gc.ca/canada_e. html> (accessed June 14, 2007).

"Welcome to the Weather Underground." *Weather Underground.* <http://www. wunderground.com/> (accessed June 14, 2007).

"Wildfire." *Federal Emergency Management Administration.* <http://www.fema. gov/hazard/wildfire/index.shtm> (accessed June 14, 2007).

Wilhelmson, Bob, et al. "Types of Thunderstorms." *University of Illinois: Weather World 2010 Project.* <http://ww2010.atmos.uiuc.edu/(Gh)/ guides/mtr/svr/type/home.rxml> (accessed June 14, 2007).

"World Meteorological Organization Homepage." *World Meteorological Organization: A United Nations Specialized Agency.* <http://www.wmo.> (accessed June 14, 2007).

Index

Numerals in *italic type* indicate volume number. Items in **boldface** indicate main entries. Graphic elements (photos, graphs, illustrations) are denoted by (ill.). Tables are denoted by *t*.

B

Carlson, Avis D., *2:* 235
Cars. *See* Automobiles
Cascade Mountains volcanoes, *4:* 600, 604
Cave Creek Complex fire of 2005, *4:* 625
CAVR (Clean Air Visibility Rule), *5:* 788
Cb. *See* Cumulonimbus clouds
Cc (Cirrocumulus clouds), *1:* 116–18, 116 (ill.)
CDC (U.S. Centers for Disease Control), *5:* 771
Cedar fire of 2003, *4:* 625, 635
Celsius, Anders, *5:* 668
Celsius temperature scale, *5:* 668
Cenozoic era, *1:* 90–92; *5:* 733–36, 738 (ill.)
Centers for Disease Control, U.S., *5:* 771
Central America. *See also specific countries*
 El Niño effects, *2:* 286–87, 301–2
 El norte wind, *3:* 446
 Papagayo wind, *3:* 435–36
Centralia, Illinois coal beds, *4:* 636
Centre Nationale d'Etudes Spatiales (France), *2:* 318; *5:* 700
CFFP (Cooperative Forest Fire Prevention), *4:* 651
Chaos theory, *5:* 663
Chapparal vegetation, wildfires and, *4:* 640
Charge distribution (lightning), *4:* 521–25, 522 (ill.)
Charles, Jacques Alexandre César, *1:* 11
Charles' Law, *1:* 11
Chasing El Niño (television program), *2:* 315
Chasing the Monsoon (Frater), *3:* 466, 477
Cherrapunjji, India rainfall, *3:* 471
Chertoff, Michael, *3:* 381
Chicago
 blizzards, *2:* 198 (ill.), 199
 fuel cell buses, *5:* 803
 microbursts, *4:* 531
 stratus clouds, *1:* 111 (ill.)
Chickens, feather loss, *4:* 554
Chile, significant weather events, *2:* 287; *4:* 575, 584
China
 floods, *3:* 332
 hailstones, *1:* 158
 landslides, *3:* 402–3, 412
 ozone regulation, *5:* 797
 smog, *5:* 776 (ill.)
 Yellow River flood, *3:* 331, 331 (ill.)
China clay, from volcanoes, *4:* 609

Chinook wall clouds, *3:* 438
Chinook winds, *3:* 437–38, 451
Chlorofluorocarbons, *5:* 760, 793–94, 796–97, 799
Choquette, Sid, *3:* 395, 397
Chroma key, *5:* 716
Ci (Cirrus clouds), *1:* 43 (ill.), 114–15, 115 (ill.)
Cimabue (Artist), *2:* 267
Cincinnati Enquirer, 3: 332
Cinder cones, *4:* 601 (ill.), 602
Circle of Fire (Pacific Ocean), *2:* 264; *4:* 602–3, 603 (ill.)
Cirriform clouds, *1:* 107; *4:* 490
Cirrocumulus clouds (Cc), *1:* 116–18, 116 (ill.)
Cirrostratus clouds (Cs), *1:* 115–16
Cirrus clouds (Ci), *1:* 43 (ill.), 114–15, 115 (ill.)
Cirrus floccus clouds, *1:* 125
Cirrus uncinus clouds, *1:* 125, 126 (ill.)
CLASS (Comprehensive Large Array-data Stewardship System), *5:* 702–3
Classification systems
 air masses, *1:* 23–25
 climates, *1:* 63
 clouds, *1:* 107–10, 109*t;* *5:* 684
 hurricanes, *2:* 291; *3:* 365, 379–80
 tornadoes, *4:* 530–31
Clean Air Act of 1956 (UK), *5:* 775
Clean Air Act (U.S.)
 acid rain, *5:* 791
 air quality index, *5:* 781–82
 history, *5:* 786–88
 ozone regulation, *5:* 797–98
Clean Air Interstate Rule (CAIR), *5:* 788
Clean Air Mercury Rule (CAMR), *5:* 788
Clean Air Visibility Rule (CAVR), *5:* 788
Clean Water (song), *3:* 333
Clear skies, defined, *5:* 684
Climate, *1:* 57–106. *See also* Humid tropical climates; Subtropical climates
 defined, *1:* 57–58; *5:* 727
 dry types, *1:* 64, 69–73, 70 (ill.), 73 (ill.), 86; *2:* 243–44
 mountain types, *1:* 84–86, 85 (ill.)
 polar types, *1:* 60, 62, 80–84, 82 (ill.); *5:* 794–95
 precipitation role, *1:* 60, 62–63, 62 (ill.); *5:* 730
 semiarid, *1:* 72, 86; *2:* 229

Colorado
  avalanches, *1:* 155
  Big Thompson River flood, *3:* 328 (ill.), 329
  chinook wind, *3:* 438
  Storm King Mountain fire, *4:* 619
  wildfires, *4:* 619, 622–23, 624, 625, 637, 644 (ill.), 649
Columbia Complex fire of 2006, *4:* 626
Columbia Gorge wind, *3:* 436
Combustion, *4:* 631–32, 632 (ill.)
Comet Ikeya-Zhang, *5:* 730 (ill.)
Comet Shoemaker-Levy, *1:* 99; *5:* 744–45
Comets and climate change, *1:* 98–99; *5:* 731, 743–45, 744 (ill.)
Commonwealth Bay, Antarctica winds, *3:* 453
Composite cones, *4:* 590, 602
Comprehensive Large Array-data Stewardship System (CLASS), *5:* 702–3
Compressional warming, *1:* 39; *3:* 435, 437
Computer modeling
  blizzards, *2:* 199–200
  El Niño events, *2:* 316 (ill.)
  future trends, *5:* 723–24
  global sea temperatures, *1:* 52 (ill.)
  industrial pollution, *5:* 777 (ill.)
  uses, *5:* 700–703, 701 (ill.)
Condensation. *See also* Clouds
  dew formation, *1:* 34–35
  fog formation, *1:* 36–37; *3:* 337
  frost formation, *1:* 35–36
  nuclei for, *1:* 36, 44
Conduction, *1:* 4
Conelets (volcanoes), *4:* 597, 598 (ill.)
Cones (volcanoes), *4:* 597, 598 (ill.), 601 (ill.), 602
Connecticut blizzards, *2:* 188, 190
Conservation of angular momentum, *1:* 29–30
Conservation tillage, *2:* 248
Construction measures
  earthquakes, *2:* 279, 280 (ill.), 281
  hurricanes, *3:* 353
  landslides, *3:* 398, 412–13, 413 (ill.), 415
  tsunamis, *4:* 581–82
  volcanoes, *4:* 612
  wildfires, *4:* 652
Constructive interference, *4:* 496

Continental air masses (cA), *1:* 23
Continental drift
  climate change history, *1:* 88, 89, 90, 93–95, 94 (ill.); *5:* 733–34, 737–40, 738 (ill.)
  plate tectonics, *2:* 262
Continental polar air masses (cP), *1:* 24
Contrails, *1:* 130–31, 132 (ill.)
Control lines (fires), *4:* 645–46
Convection
  air stability and, *1:* 43
  defined, *1:* 4
  Earth's interior, *2:* 261–62
  experiment, *3:* 470
Convective cells, *4:* 509
Convergence and divergence
  defined, *1:* 21–22
  hurricanes, *3:* 366–67
  thunderstorms, *4:* 503, 509, 511–12
Cool deserts, *1:* 70
Cooling, expansional, *1:* 39
Cooperative Forest Fire Prevention (CFFP), *4:* 651
Copper, from volcanoes, *4:* 609
Coral reef bleaching, *2:* 310
Core, Earth's, *2:* 261; *4:* 596, 597 (ill.)
Coriolis, Gaspard-Gustave de, *1:* 14
Coriolis effect
  hurricanes, *3:* 364, 367
  ocean currents, *1:* 51
  wind, *1:* 14–15
Coronas, *4:* 495–96, 496 (ill.)
Corridor of Greenery avalanches (Peru), *2:* 163 (ill.), 164–69, 164 (ill.), 170
Costello, Elvis, *3:* 333
Counterclockwise wind rotation, *1:* 15
Cows, rain prediction and, *5:* 665, 665 (ill.)
Coxwell, Robert, *1:* 10
cP (Continental polar air masses), *1:* 24
Cramer fire of 2003, *4:* 625
Crashes, storm-related, *1:* 142; *2:* 248; *4:* 531
Crater Lake, Oregon, *4:* 601
Craters
  from asteroids, *5:* 743
  volcanoes, *4:* 597–98, 598 (ill.), 601, 601 (ill.)
Credits, carbon dioxide, *5:* 767
Crepuscular rays, *4:* 482–83, 483 (ill.)
Crescenti dunes, *3:* 452–54, 454 (ill.)

Glaze (ice), *1:* 142, 143 (ill.), 146

Glick, Patty, *5:* 762

Global climate change. *See* Climate change; Global warming

Global Lagrangian Drifters, *2:* 316

Global nature of weather forecasting, *5:* 659

Global pressure patterns, *1:* 18–19

Global Seismographic Network (GSN), *2:* 279

Global warming. *See also* Climate change; Human influences on weather and climate
blizzards and, *2:* 195–97
causes, *5:* 750–51, 757–61, 759 (ill.), 764–65
defined, *2:* 310–11; *5:* 750
droughts and, *2:* 216
effects, *5:* 751–52, 761–64, 762 (ill.), 764 (ill.)
El Niño and, *2:* 310–14
future trends, *5:* 767–68
human factors, *5:* 750–51, 764–65
international talks on, *5:* 765–67
ozone depletion and, *5:* 798
rising sea levels and, *5:* 752–57, 754 (ill.), 756 (ill.), 757 (ill.)
wildfires and, *4:* 641–43

Global wind patterns, *1:* 16–18

Glories, *4:* 497–98

Goblin Valley ventifacts, *3:* 456

GOES (Geostationary Operational Environmental Satellite), *2:* 200 (ill.); *5:* 698, 699 (ill.)

Goethe, Johann Wolfgang von, *4:* 498

Goff, James, *4:* 569

Gohei (Japanese squire), *4:* 582–83

Gondwana (supercontinent), *1:* 88; *5:* 733

Gore, Al, *5:* 751, 785

Gorham, Illinois, tornado, *4:* 534, 540

Grand Banks fog, *3:* 341

Grand Forks, North Dakota, flood, *3:* 333, 333 (ill.)

The Grapes of Wrath (film), *2:* 241 (ill.)

The Grapes of Wrath (Steinbeck), *2:* 240–41

Graupel, *1:* 149; *4:* 523

Gravity winds. *See* Mountain breezes

Great Blue Norther of 11/11/11, *3:* 447

Great Britain. *See* United Kingdom

Great Depression, *2:* 235, 237–38, 237 (ill.)

Great Flood of 1993, *3:* 329

Great Mississippi River Flood of 1927, *3:* 328–29

Great Plains States. *See also* Dust Bowl of the 1930s
derechos, *3:* 449
hailstones, *1:* 157
snow accumulation, *3:* 455
thunderstorms, *4:* 511
wildfires, *4:* 625

Great Slave Lake exposed rocks, *5:* 746

Great Smog of 1952, *5:* 775

Great Smoky Mountain National Park pollution, *5:* 785, 790 (ill.)

Green algae, El Niño and, *2:* 306

Green flashes, *4:* 486

Greenhouse effect, *5:* 757–59, 759 (ill.). *See also* Global warming

Greenhouse gases. *See also specific gases*
defined, *2:* 196, 311
Kyoto Protocol, *5:* 766
types, *5:* 750, 758–61

Greenland
ice core analysis, *1:* 102; *5:* 747, 748 (ill.)
melting glaciers, *5:* 753

Griffin, Indiana, tornado, *4:* 534, 539 (ill.), 541

Gros Ventre River landslide, *3:* 404–5

Ground blizzards, *1:* 151

Ground fires, *4:* 636

Ground fog, *3:* 338, 339 (ill.)

Ground-level ozone. *See* Ozone, near-surface

Ground-to-cloud lightning, *4:* 525

Groundwater, *1:* 48; *2:* 218, 222

GSN (Global Seismographic Network), *2:* 279

Guam, El Niño and, *2:* 292

Guatemala, significant weather events, *3:* 447; *4:* 608 (ill.)

Guggenheim, Charles, *3:* 330

Gulf Coast States. *See also* Hurricane Katrina; *specific states*
floods of 2005, *3:* 333
hurricanes, *3:* 381–82

Gulfstream weather aircraft, *3:* 389, 389 (ill.); *5:* 691–92

Gust fronts, *4:* 513, 530

Gutenberg, Beno, *2:* 277–78

Gyres, *1:* 51

H

Kenya, El Niño and, *2:* 289–90

Kettering self-starters, *5:* 800

Khait, Tajikistan, landslides, *3:* 405–6

Khamsin winds, *2:* 244; *3:* 444

Kilauea volcano, *4:* 600 (ill.), 605 (ill.)

Kinetic energy. *See* Energy

King penguins, *5:* 764 (ill.)

Kiribati, climate change concerns, *5:* 756

Kite-flying experiment, *4:* 518, 519 (ill.)

Knight, Nancy, *1:* 151

Kobe earthquake of 1995 (Japan), *2:* 268–69, 269 (ill.)

Konas, *3:* 450–51

Köppen, Wladimir, *1:* 63

Köppen climate system, *1:* 63

Krakatau, Indonesia,
    tsunami, *4:* 577
    volcano eruption, *4:* 591, 601

Krill, decline of, *5:* 763

Kudloo, Tom, *5:* 691

Kyoto Conference of 1997, *5:* 765–66

Kyoto Protocol, *5:* 766

L

L waves, *2:* 265

La Niña, *3:* **417–29**
    1998 to 2000 episode, *3:* 423–28, 426 (ill.)
    defined, *3:* 417, 419
    droughts and, *2:* 216
    effects, *3:* 419 (ill.), 421–22, 425 (ill.)
    El Niño and, *3:* 417, 420, 421 (ill.), 423 (ill.)
    monitoring and forecasting, *3:* 428

Labrador Current, *3:* 341

Lahars
    defined, *3:* 406–7
    Japan, *3:* 409 (ill.)
    Mount St. Helens eruption, *3:* 399; *4:* 591–92
    as volcano hazard, *4:* 606

Lake breezes, *3:* 433

Lake-effect snow, *1:* 152, 152 (ill.)

Lakes
    acid rain effects, *5:* 791–92
    bursting of natural dams, *5:* 754–55

drought effects, *2:* 218–19
    sediment analysis, *1:* 103–4; *5:* 748–49

Laki, Iceland, volcano, *4:* 591

Land. *See* Topography

Land breezes, *1:* 48–49; *3:* 431, 433, 433 (ill.)

Land degradation. *See* Desertification

Landsat Earth survey satellites, *2:* 225–26

Landslides, *3:* **391–416**
    California, *3:* 404 (ill.), 408 (ill.), 411
    causes, *3:* 391, 403–7
    China, *3:* 412
    defined, *2:* 170; *3:* 391
    effects, *3:* 408–9
    experiment, *3:* 399
    fissures and, *2:* 266
    Frank, Canada, *3:* 393–97, 394 (ill.)
    human factors, *3:* 409–12
    Japan, *3:* 407, 408, 409 (ill.)
    Kashmir earthquake and, *2:* 260
    La Niña effects, *3:* 426, 426 (ill.)
    monitoring and forecasting, *3:* 413–15
    Papua New Guinea, *4:* 568
    Philippines, *3:* 397, 402 (ill.), 403, 414, 414 (ill.)
    recent occurrences, *3:* 397–99, 398 (ill.), 400 (ill.)
    regions of, *3:* 407–8
    safety measures, *3:* 412–13, 413 (ill.), 415
    sinkholes, *3:* 406–7, 407 (ill.)
    tsunamis and, *4:* 576
    types, *3:* 392 (ill.), 399–403
    Yosemite rockfall, *3:* 410, 410 (ill.)

Latent heat, *1:* 6, 32

Laurasia (supercontinent), *5:* 733

Laurussia (supercontinent), *1:* 88; *5:* 733

Lava
    control measures, *4:* 612
    defined, *4:* 587, 597, 599 (ill.)
    flowing, *4:* 600 (ill.)
    unusual formations, *4:* 614, 614 (ill.)

Lava domes, *4:* 602

Lava tubes, *4:* 614

Lavoisier, Antoine, *1:* 9

Lawn mowers, pollution from, *5:* 787

Lead, pollution from, *5:* 777–78

Least terns, El Niño effects, *2:* 304, 308 (ill.)

M

mA (Maritime arctic air masses), *1:* 23–24

"Mackerel sky," *1:* 116–17, 135

Macrobursts, *4:* 529–30

MAFFS (Modular Airborne Fire Fighting Systems), *4:* 626, 647, 647 (ill.)

Magma, *4:* 587, 597, 598, 598 (ill.)

Magma chambers, *4:* 598, 598 (ill.)

Magnesium, depletion of, *5:* 792

Magnitude of earthquakes, *2:* 274

Mahmoud, Omar, *2:* 212

Maine drought, *2:* 214 (ill.)

Majja Valley tree-planting project (Niger), *2:* 212

Malaria, *2:* 309; *3:* 328

Malaysia, significant weather events, *2:* 285–86; *4:* 566 (ill.)

Mali drought, *2:* 209 (ill.)

Malibu, California wildfires, *4:* 635

Mammals

    boreal forests, *1:* 80

    oceans, *2:* 304–5

    steppe climates, *1:* 73

    tundra climates, *1:* 82

Mammatus clouds, *1:* 127–28, 128 (ill.); *4:* 542 (ill.)

Manchu River Dam collapse of 1979, *3:* 474, 474 (ill.)

Manila, Philippines, monsoon, *3:* 450 (ill.)

Mann Gulch fire of 1949, *4:* 617–19, 618 (ill.)

Mantle, Earth's, *2:* 261–62; *4:* 596, 597 (ill.)

Manufactured housing, tornadoes and, *4:* 553–54, 556, 556 (ill.)

Maps, weather. *See* Weather maps

March of the Penguins (film), *1:* 81

Mares' tails (clouds), *1:* 16 (ill.), 125

Marin County, California, wildfires, *4:* 635

Marine animals

    El Niño effects, *2:* 303–5

    fossils of, *5:* 747

    global warming disruptions, *5:* 762–64

Marine climates, *1:* 64, 75, 86

Marine forecasts, *5:* 721, 722

Maritime arctic air masses (mA), *1:* 23–24

Maritime polar air masses (mP), *1:* 24

Maritime tropical air masses (mT), *1:* 25

Martin, Joe "Smokey," *4:* 651

Mature stage of thunderstorms, *4:* 504 (ill.), 506–8

Mature stage of tornadoes, *4:* 547

Mauna Loa volcano, *4:* 604, 605 (ill.)

Maunder, E. W., *1:* 100; *5:* 746

Maunder minimum, *1:* 100; *5:* 746

Mawson, Douglas, *3:* 453

Maximum thermometers, *5:* 671–72, 672 (ill.)

MCC (Mesoscale convective complexes), *4:* 511

McMath-Pierce Solar Telescope, *5:* 745 (ill.)

McNally fire of 2002, *4:* 635

Mean temperature, *1:* 59; *5:* 704, 728

Media weather reports. *See* Weather reports

Mediterranean climates

    defined, *1:* 64, 75–77, 76 (ill.)

    levanters, *3:* 450

    in the U.S., *1:* 86

    waterspouts, *4:* 553, 553 (ill.)

Medium-range forecasts, *5:* 662, 664

Meghna River, *3:* 462

Melting

    glaciers, *5:* 752–57, 754 (ill.)

    hailstones, *1:* 157

    ice crystals in air, *1:* 31, 137

    latent heat, *1:* 6

    road salt, *1:* 148; *2:* 201–2

Meltwater equivalent, *5:* 682

Mercalli, Giuseppe, *2:* 275

Mercalli earthquake scale, *2:* 275–77

Mercury barometers, *5:* 677, 678, 680 (ill.)

Mesocyclones, *4:* 516, 542–43, 542 (ill.), 543 (ill.)

Mesoscale convective complexes (MCC), *4:* 511

Mesoscale winds. *See* Local winds

Mesosphere, *1:* 9

Mesozoic era, *1:* 88–90; *5:* 733

Meteorologists, *5:* 655, 658 (ill.)

Meteorology, defined, *5:* 655. *See also* Forecasting

Methane emissions, *5:* 760–61, 779

Methyl bromide, *5:* 797, 798–99

Methyl chloroform, *5:* 797, 798

Mexico

    El Niño effects, *2:* 286–87, 291

    hurricanes, *3:* 373–74

eruptions, *4:* 587, 588, 588 (ill.), 590–91, 594–96; *5:* 743 (ill.)

flooded logging camp, *4:* 606 (ill.)

lahars from, *3:* 399, 406–7; *4:* 591–92

Mount Tambora volcano, *4:* 610; *5:* 742

Mount Vesuvius volcano, *1:* 98 (ill.); *4:* 591, 594–95, 595 (ill.)

Mount Wai'-'ale'ale rain shadow, *1:* 49–50

Mount Washington, New Hampshire winds, *3:* 453

Mountain breezes, *3:* 433–34

Mountain climates, *1:* 84–86, 85 (ill.)

Mountain recreation, *2:* 176–77; *5:* 721

Mountain thunderstorms, *4:* 509

Mountain-wave clouds

air layers, *1:* 133 (ill.)

banner cloud, *1:* 130 (ill.)

lenticular cloud, *1:* 129 (ill.)

orographic stratus, *1:* 141 (ill.)

types, *1:* 128–30

Mountains

Brocken spectres, *4:* 498, 499 (ill.)

continental drift and, *1:* 94–95; *5:* 739–40

katabatic winds, *3:* 434–40, 434 (ill.), 439 (ill.)

mountain and valley breezes, *3:* 433–34, 434 (ill.)

upslope fog, *3:* 344–45, 344 (ill.)

from volcanoes, *4:* 587

weather patterns, *1:* 49–50

Moving fronts, *1:* 25

mP (Maritime polar air masses), *1:* 24

mT (Maritime tropical air masses), *1:* 25

Mudflow landslides

defined, *3:* 392 (ill.), 401

Italy, *3:* 398, 398 (ill.)

lahars, *3:* 399, 406–7, 409 (ill.); *4:* 591–92, 606

Santa Ana winds and, *3:* 440

Mugginess, *5:* 704–5, 707. *See also* Relative humidity

Muir Glacier, *5:* 734 (ill.)

Multi-vortex tornadoes, *4:* 547, 547 (ill.)

Multicell thunderstorms, defined, *4:* 509

Murphysboro, Illinois, tornado, *4:* 534–35, 537–41, 537 (ill.), 538 (ill.)

Mushroom rocks, *3:* 456

Music on floods, *3:* 333

N

Nakisony, Fabian, *4:* 570

Naming system (hurricanes), *3:* 357–58, 386–88, 387*t*

NAO (North Atlantic Oscillation), *2:* 300

NASA (National Aeronautics and Space Administration)

aircraft pollution research, *5:* 787

glacier research, *5:* 753

weather satellites, *2:* 318; *5:* 698, 699

National Center for Atmospheric Research, *4:* 558

National Center of Space Studies (France), *2:* 318

National Centers for Environmental Prediction, *3:* 428

National Data Buoy Center, *4:* 581

National Drought Mitigation Center, *2:* 217

National Guard firefighting assistance, *4:* 623

National Hurricane Center, *3:* 383, 388

National Incident Information Center, *4:* 626

National Oceanic and Atmospheric Administration (NOAA)

computer modeling, *5:* 701–3

hurricane research, *3:* 389; *5:* 691–92

Internet weather reports, *5:* 716

La Niña predictions, *3:* 428

satellites, *2:* 200 (ill.); *5:* 698–700, 699 (ill.)

TOGA/TAO research, *2:* 315, 317

on tornadoes, *4:* 554

vessels for data collection, *2:* 318; *5:* 692, 693 (ill.)

Weather Radio, *4:* 560; *5:* 715–16

National Renewable Energy Laboratory, *5:* 808

National Tsunami Hazard Mitigation Program (NTHMP), *4:* 581

National Weather Association, *5:* 713

National Weather Service (NWS)

on blizzards, *2:* 185, 189

computer modeling, *5:* 700–703, 701 (ill.)

Doppler radar analysis, *2:* 198–99; *5:* 695, 695 (ill.)

landslide monitoring and forecasting, *3:* 413–14

as national data coordinator, *5:* 661

radiosonde returns, *5:* 690–91

Roosevelt, Franklin Delano, *2:* 235
Rossby waves, *2:* 294
Rotation of the Earth. *See* Earth's rotation
Runout zones (avalanches), *2:* 175

S

S waves, *2:* 264–65, 266 (ill.)
Safe rooms, *4:* 554
Safeguarding the Ozone Layer and the Global Climate System (IPCC), *5:* 798
Safety measures. *See also* Emergency preparedness; Health issues
   avalanches, *2:* 177–80, 178 (ill.), 179 (ill.), 180 (ill.), 182
   blizzards, *1:* 154; *2:* 200–202, 201 (ill.), 204–5
   dust storms, *2:* 248–49
   earthquakes, *2:* 280–82, 280 (ill.)
   floods, *3:* 326
   heat waves, *2:* 224
   hurricanes, *3:* 380, 383–86
   lake-bursts, *5:* 755
   landslides, *3:* 412–13, 413 (ill.)
   lightning, *4:* 517
   tornadoes, *4:* 554, 561–62
   tsunamis, *4:* 581–85
   volcanoes, *4:* 611–14
   wildfires, *4:* 649–52, 651 (ill.)
Saffir, Herbert, *3:* 379
Saffir-Simpson Hurricane Damage Potential Scale, *2:* 291; *3:* 365, 379–80
Sahara region (Africa)
   dust storms, *2:* 243–44
   winds, *3:* 443–45, 444 (ill.), 445 (ill.)
Sahel region drought (Africa), *2:* 207–13, 209 (ill.), 210 (ill.), 213 (ill.); *3:* 474–75
Sairere, John, *4:* 569
Salt
   drinking water salination, *5:* 756
   for roads, *1:* 148; *2:* 201–2
   water freezing point experiment, *2:* 202
Saltation, *2:* 242; *3:* 451–52, 452(ill.)
San Andreas Fault, *2:* 254–55, 254 (ill.)

San Francisco, California,
   earthquakes, *2:* 251–58, 253 (ill.), 254 (ill.)
   sea fog, *3:* 341–42
Sand blows, *2:* 266
Sand dunes, *3:* 452–54, 454 (ill.)
Sand formations, *3:* 451–54, 452 (ill.), 454 (ill.)
Sand ripples, *3:* 454
Sand storms
   desert winds, *3:* 440–41, 443, 443 (ill.), 444 (ill.)
   vs. dust storms, *2:* 229–30
   types, *2:* 242–44
Sanriku, Japan, tsunamis, *4:* 578, 581 (ill.)
Santa Ana winds
   health issues, *3:* 451
   overview, *3:* 438–40
   wildfires, *3:* 439 (ill.); *4:* 635, 638–39
Santa River (Peru), *2:* 164, 168
Santorini, Greece, volcano, *4:* 596, 597
Sastrugi snow ripples, *3:* 455, 456–57
Satellite monitoring
   drought conditions, *2:* 225–26
   GOES system, *2:* 200 (ill.)
   hurricanes, *3:* 389–90
   oceans, *2:* 318
   television report images, *5:* 714
   uses, *2:* 198; *5:* 696–98, 697 (ill.)
   wildfires, *4:* 622 (ill.)
Saturation point, *1:* 32, 39–40
Savanna climates, *1:* 64, 68–69, 69 (ill.)
Sc (Stratocumulus clouds), *1:* 110, 114 (ill.)
Scarps, *2:* 265
Scars, rockfall, *3:* 392 (ill.)
Schaefer, Vincent, *1:* 144
Scientific Assessment of Ozone Depletion: 2002 (WMO), *5:* 796
Scrub brush, *1:* 85 (ill.)
Scud (Stratus fractus clouds), *1:* 124
Sea animals. *See* Marine animals
Sea breezes, *1:* 48–49; *3:* 431, 433, 433 (ill.)
Sea fog, *3:* 341–42
Sea Islands hurricane of 1893, *3:* 368
Sea level
   rising, *5:* 752–57, 754 (ill.), 756 (ill.), 757 (ill.), 758
   temperature adjustment, *1:* 59

Seafloor movement, *4:* 577–78, 597

Seagoing vessels. *See* Watercraft

Seals, El Niño and, *2:* 304–5

Search and Rescue Satellite-Aided Tracking System, *5:* 700

Search-and-rescue satellite programs, *5:* 700

Seas. *See* Oceans

Seasat, *5:* 700

Seasonable weather, forecasting, *5:* 688–89

Seasons

air masses, *1:* 24, 25

arctic climates, *1:* 83–84

changes in, *1:* 1–2

climate type, *1:* 64

deserts, *1:* 70

Earth's rotation, *1:* 95–97; *5:* 741–42

high/low pressure systems, *1:* 19

humid subtropical climates, *1:* 74

for hurricanes, *3:* 364–65

La Niña effects, *3:* 422, 427–28

Marine climates, *1:* 75

Mediterranean climates, *1:* 75

monsoon regions, *1:* 66, 67; *3:* 449–50, 468–71

ocean temperatures, *1:* 51

precession of equinoxes, *1:* 96 (ill.)

savannas, *1:* 68

storm paths, *1:* 30

subpolar climates, *1:* 79

temperate climates, *1:* 77, 78

tropical rain forests, *1:* 65

tundra climates, *1:* 81

for wildfires, *4:* 638

winds, *1:* 21

Seawalls, *4:* 582

Sebago Lake drought (Maine), *2:* 214 (ill.)

Second Assessment Report (AR 2), *3:* 333

Secondary air pollutants, *5:* 776

Secondary body waves (S), *2:* 264–65, 266 (ill.)

Secondary rainbows, *4:* 494–95

Sector plate snowflakes, *1:* 147, 150 (ill.); *2:* 192

Sediment analysis, *1:* 103–4; *5:* 742, 748–49, 749 (ill.)

Seif dunes, *3:* 454

Seismic waves, *2:* 264–65, 266 (ill.)

Seismographs, *2:* 259 (ill.), 274–75, 276 (ill.), 278 (ill.)

Seismology

earthquake hazard map, *2:* 277 (ill.)

Mercalli scale, *2:* 275–77

Richter scale, *2:* 251, 277–78

seismographs, *2:* 259 (ill.), 274–75, 276 (ill.), 278 (ill.)

seismoscopes, *2:* 274, 275 (ill.)

for volcanoes, *4:* 611

Seismoscopes, *2:* 274, 275 (ill.)

Semiarid climates. *See also* Dry climates; Steppe climates

defined, *1:* 72

dust storm susceptibility, *2:* 229

in the U.S., *1:* 86

Semipermanent pressure systems, *1:* 19

SES (Soil Erosion Service), *2:* 239

Severe blizzards, *1:* 151

Severe Thunderstorm Electrification and Precipitation Study (STEPS), *4:* 559

Severe thunderstorms, *4:* 511–16, 514 (ill.), 515 (ill.), 516 (ill.)

Severe weather alerts. *See* Weather alerts

Shake and bakes (portable shelters), *4:* 650

Shamal winds, *2:* 244; *3:* 445

Shear, wind. *See* Wind shear

Sheds, avalanche, *2:* 178, 178 (ill.)

Sheet lightning, *4:* 526

Shelf clouds, *4:* 513

Shelters

for fighting fires, *4:* 650

for home weather centers, *5:* 669–70, 670 (ill.)

safe rooms, *4:* 554

tornadoes, *4:* 561

Shield cones, *4:* 602

Ships. *See* Watercraft

Shoemaker-Levy comet, *1:* 99

Short-range forecasts, *5:* 662, 664

Shoshone fire of 1988, *4:* 638 (ill.)

Show Low fire of 2002, *4:* 624

Showers, household, reduced-flow, *2:* 222

Showers, rain, *1:* 140–41

Shrinking stage of tornadoes, *4:* 547

Sicily, Italy, volcano, *4:* 612, 612 (ill.)

T

U

2/13/08 $ 300.00

LONGWOOD PUBLIC LIBRARY
Middle Country Road
Middle Island, NY 11953
(631) 924-6400
LIBRARY HOURS

Monday-Friday	9:30 a.m. - 9:00 p.m.
Saturday	9:30 a.m. - 5:00 p.m.
Sunday (Sept-June)	1:00 p.m. - 5:00 p.m.